About the author

Janet Menzies is a member of the Guild of Health Writers, and the bestselling author of *The D.I.Y. Diet*. Her career on national newspapers has spanned 15 years, working on the *Daily Telegraph*, the *Daily Mail, Hello!* magazine and the *Daily Express*, where she was Woman's Editor.

Also by Janet Menzies

The D.I.Y. Diet

The Japanese Diet

Janet Menzies

Hodder & Stoughton

First published in Great Britain in 1996
by Hodder and Stoughton
A division of Hodder Headline PLC

10 9 8 7 6 5 4 3 2 1

British Library Cataloguing in Publication Data

Menzies, Janet
The Japanese diet
1. Diet – Japan 2. Nutrition – Japan
I. title
613.2'0952

ISBN 0 340 67200 5

Typeset by Palimpsest Book Production Limited,
Polmont, Stirlingshire
Printed and bound in Great Britain by
Cox and Wyman Ltd, Reading, Berkshire

Hodder and Stoughton
A division of Hodder Headline PLC
338 Euston Road
London NW1 3BH

CONTENTS

INTRODUCTION

What an adventure it was twenty-odd years ago when my mother and I first started cooking Japanese and Oriental foods. Liverpool, where we lived, had a thriving Oriental community based on the edge of the town centre between the old bombed-out church and the Victorian docks area. The two of us used to climb into my mother's blue sports car and zoom in from the suburbs, cresting the San Francisco-like Mount Pleasant hill and descending into an area which was essentially unchanged since Onedin Line days.

Little did we realise that we were also entering a fairly notorious red light and illegal gambling district. Perhaps my mother had an inkling, because certain parking spots meant that I would be shuffled out of the car and up the street rather more quickly than others. In the afternoons you could hear from the upper floors of the mouldering Victorian buildings the clack, clack, clack of mah-jong tablets (often Chinese restaurants changed hands with overnight rapidity, and mah-jong gambling was the reason). On the ground floors of these buildings, once the homes and offices of the merchant princes, were what my mother and I had come for: Oriental grocers' stores.

In those days even soy sauce was something of a rarity and things like dried Japanese mushrooms, bottled plum sauce and transparent cellophane noodles were absolutely unheard of. If you wanted them you had to go to a real Chinese or Japanese grocers, run by a real, basically non-English speaking, Chinese or Japanese family.

What extraordinary places these shops were, their shelves stacked with all manner of cans and packs identified only by calligraphy symbols, their freezers filled with what looked like portions of frozen sea-monster – all tentacles and suckers. And what triumphs and disasters Mum and I encountered in our quest to separate the delicious from the inedible.

Nowadays Oriental food is commonplace. All the ingredients you will need on the Japanese Diet you will be able to find at your local branch of Tesco. Although far more convenient, in some ways it's a bit of a shame, because Oriental grocers are such interesting places. Today they are run by second or third generation Chinese or Japanese who are likely to greet you in fluent cockney or scouse. The imported goods now all have labels stuck on telling you in English what they are. But when my mother and I got interested it was all Japanese characters or if you were lucky an incomprehensible "English" translation about "skins of the gluten" or "pressed laver". Some of the ingredients we were looking for were recognisable by their appearance. A helpful photograph on a can depicting a Chinese straw mushroom or a pretty Japanese bamboo stem meant a safe buy. But most of our Oriental shopping resembled the vast gambles going on upstairs over the mah-jong table. What about the time we opened a packet to discover it packed with round, white apparently completely inedible marble-like things, which I now know were a great delicacy, lotus seeds, and the reason our shopping had been so expensive. There were triumphs too – the discovery of dried shrimps which made up into the most marvellous seafood soup; bringing weird-looking "wooden ear" mushrooms to life by soaking them. I won't even mention the epic struggle to learn how to deal with seaweed in all its various forms – particularly since it is not a compulsory part of the Japanese Diet. But we did discover that the more-ish butchers' grass stuff called seaweed in Chinese restaurants is actually deep-fried cabbage, and that real seaweed is in fact far easier to use in cooking than you might imagine – once you know how (see page 77).

It was all splendid fun, and made a huge difference to my adult approach to cookery and food. But it was only recently that I discovered the health and slimming benefits of Oriental food, especially Japanese cuisine.

I had been researching a major publication about the chronic diseases which have developed in the Western world in the twentieth century. In particular I was writing about the possible causes of coronary heart disease and cancer and how we might prevent them. During the course of interviewing leading experts including Professor Richard Peto (who helped discover the link between cancer and smoking) and Professor Anthony Shaper (a founder of heart disease research), I was referred again and again to statistics about Japan being the only developed Western-style country not to suffer from these "Western" diseases.

All the researchers were trying to find out why the Japanese seem to be so much less prone to heart disease and most forms of cancer than we are. I found this interesting, and included the statistics in my book, but it wasn't until I was interviewing breast-cancer campaign Alice Mahon MP, that it really clicked. Talking to me about one of her constituents who had overcome breast cancer, she mentioned in passing: "Of course, she was on a Japanese diet."

Instinctively I knew this was the answer: the Japanese diet. As soon as I had finished my health risks book, I started my research all over again – this time looking for evidence to link the Japanese diet with their general health, and of course, slimness. The evidence was certainly there. I realised that eating a Japanese-style diet could help all of us. Here are just a few of those benefits.

FOR MEN:

Coronary heart disease hits 96 per cent fewer men in Japan than in Britain and overall Japanese rates of heart disease are the lowest in the affluent world

FOR WOMEN:

In Britain breast cancer rates are 28 per 100,000 but in Japan only 6 in 100,000 women suffer

FOR SLIMMERS:

People who have difficulty slimming can lose weight by eating Japanese food which is rich in iodine and so stimulates the metabolism

FOR OLDER PEOPLE:
Rates of arthritis among Japanese are very low and it is usual for general good health to continue well into old age

FOR ALL OF US:
The Japanese are a generally slim and healthy nation
Colorectal (bowel) cancer rates in Japan are much lower than in most wealthy countries

All these long-term health benefits are wonderful – especially if you have risk factors for cancer or heart disease – but what most of us are really concerned about is getting and staying slim. So when I devised the Japanese Diet, I knew it would not be enough just to write about its health benefits.

What we are all looking for is a simple, really effective way to get into shape and keep that shape, at the same time as feeling generally healthier.

That is exactly what the Japanese Diet will show you how to do. Although based directly on the national Japanese diet, it has been adapted to make it easier to understand and prepare; simple and fun to follow; and especially effective in making you look good and feel great.

Because the Japanese Diet is based on a national cuisine, rather than being a specific slimming diet, you will find it far less restrictive than other diets you may have tried. On this diet you can:

○ eat fried food
○ forget calories
○ eat as much as you want
○ eat out
○ enjoy your meals

After all, when I first discovered Japanese eating, all those years ago in Liverpool, slimming had nothing to do with it. Above all it was fun, an adventure. Which is exactly what I hope you will discover when you go on the Japanese Diet.

For a diet to be truly successful it has to be about much more than getting thin or eating less. We all know that food means much more to us than just staying alive or keeping healthy. Most diets try to ignore this fact, but the Japanese Diet positively welcomes it.

As you learn about Japanese cooking and eating, you will also discover a whole new culture and way of looking at life. Many health-giving ingredients of Japanese food are also used in beauty preparations for skin care and cosmetics, so it is a very small step from slimming to overhauling your beauty regime. While you are working towards achieving your ideal figure, the Japanese beauty tips in this book will help you take some short cuts and cheer you up when things seem tough.

The preparation and presentation of Japanese food places as much emphasis on enjoying its appearance, fragrance and texture as on actually eating it, and this stress on other sensory pleasures apart from eating goes right through Japanese culture. So you will find sections on treats like Japanese baths, which are a wonderful way of relaxing and helping yourself to feel better.

For male slimmers especially, this discovery of other pleasures than eating can be a tremendous help. While women can cheer themselves up by going to the hairdressers, buying a new lipstick or leafing through a magazine, different sexual stereotypes mean that men have traditionally only had the blow-out (preferably curry) or the drinking binge or the motorway ton-up as their outlets – none of them exactly advisable. Following the Japanese Diet, men will discover all sorts of new methods for relieving stress and banishing blues, from T'ai Chi martial arts exercises to techniques for dealing with difficult workplace situations.

To the Japanese, what they eat, and the way they eat it, is one element in a wider context of self-nurturing to promote all-round well-being. If you can discover the secrets of creating personal well-being, you will rapidly find that the question of slimming becomes irrelevant. This adventure into the cuisine and culture of Japan is aimed at achieving exactly that goal.

Great travellers tell you that it is only by visiting other lands and other peoples that you come to a true understanding of your own land and your own self. I hope this voyage into the Japanese Diet will do the same for you.

Personally I'll never forget my early escapades in Oriental cuisine. With the benefit of some of my more hilarious (and disastrous) experiences, I think your trip will be more enjoyable and less hair-raising than mine. But it should still be a great adventure, and one that could change your whole life.

PART ONE

1

HEALTH BENEFITS FOR MEN AND WOMEN

The Japanese Diet and Breast Cancer

Breast cancer is the most common cancer among women in this country (closely followed by lung cancer), and sadly its rates have been rising continuously at about one per cent per year for the last twenty-five years. Soon one in ten women may be confronted with a diagnosis of breast cancer.

> **At present one woman in 12 in the UK develops breast cancer at some time in her life compared with only one in 60 Japanese women**

Nor is breast cancer a worry for just British women. With 570,000 new cases in the world each year, breast cancer is still the most frequent malignant cancer among women, and world-wide it accounts for 18 per cent of all female cancers.

Yet these statistics are not mirrored in Japan. Among Japanese women the overall rate of breast cancer is only a fifth of what it is in Britain and the United States. Scientists are pretty sure this is due to the Japanese lifestyle, especially the way of eating, because studies of migrants from Japan to America (and the US state of Hawaii) show that the rates of breast cancer in migrants reach that of the host country within one or two generations. This indicates that factors like diet and lifestyle are of greater importance than genetic factors. More support for this theory has come from the fact that as younger Japanese people have turned away from the traditional diet of their parents towards an American-style "burger" way of eating, so their rates of breast cancer, other cancers and heart disease have started to move up towards (but still below) Western levels.

In Britain breast cancer mortality rates are 492 deaths per million of the population

---

Medical researchers in Britain are especially keen to find out more about how the Japanese are beating breast cancer because Britain has the highest death rate from breast cancer in the world. There are nearly 31,500 new cases every year in the UK and more than 15,000 deaths – one in five of all female cancer deaths.

Unfortunately Britain has a particularly poor record when it comes to the treatment of breast cancer, and recovery from it. In this country the rate of those women surviving at least five years after a diagnosis is only 62 per cent – one of the worst rates in the world.

Campaigns are being led by MP Alice Mahon and other women in order to improve the research into and treatment of breast cancer in this country. One of the first areas of research is how Japanese-style eating seems to give protection from breast cancer.

At present there are approximately 30,000 new breast-cancer cases every year

---

Dr Tim Key of the Imperial Cancer Research Fund's (ICRF) Cancer Epidemiology Unit at Oxford University is leading a major research initiative called the EPIC project. He told me: "The link between diet and breast cancer is very complicated but here at the unit we certainly believe that we will discover some connection between a diet high in fat and low in vegetables and fruit, and breast cancer."

Professor Karol Sikora, one of London's foremost cancer special-ists, agrees: "The rate of breast cancer follows closely the daily average fat consumption from country to country."

In Japan only 24 per cent of energy intake comes from fat, while in Britain it is 40 per cent. But as with heart disease, the picture is more complicated than this. Not just how much fat you eat, but the overall quality of your diet almost certainly plays a part in the risks of contracting breast cancer. Some scientists believe that faulty diet may increase risk by about one and a half times. Dr Takeshi Hirayoma of the National Cancer Research Institute in Tokyo looked at meat intake and found that women eating meat daily were four times more likely to suffer breast cancer than those eating little or no meat.

But researchers like Tim Key are suggesting that eating extra vegetables and fruit may be as important as not eating too much meat and fat.

It is too early for official research to have come up with any conclusions about this yet, but many women already believe that a Japanese-style diet is important in fighting breast cancer. Allison Coates was diagnosed as having breast cancer at the age of twenty-five and decided to set up a support group when she found that most of the other breast cancer patients she met via treatment or existing support networks, were much older than her, and had a different outlook and problems.

Her support group Bosom Friends now has around ninety-five members, and is campaigning for breast screening for all women, not just those of post-menopausal age. Some of the group have been experimenting with Japanese-style eating.

Sue Patterson is one who firmly believes in its benefits. She first went to the doctor with concerns about a lump in her breast nearly two years before she was eventually diagnosed with cancer, yet she could find no one who would take the problem seriously. The net result was that by the time it was diagnosed, the cancer was at an advanced stage and Sue was given a bleak prognosis. Sue had heard about the apparent success of a very strict version of the Japanese Diet called macrobiotic eating, combined with another Japanese technique, shiatsu massage. After meeting a British expert in macrobiotic eating, Simon Brown, she went on a diet of grains, pulses and vegetables heavily influenced by Japanese ways of eating.

Three years after being told she was terminally ill, Sue is now in remission from breast cancer, and believes her diet has played an important part in this recovery. She says: "I started the special diet three years ago when my breast cancer was diagnosed at an advanced stage. Today I have recovered from the cancer and I really think it is down to the diet."

But she acknowledges that the mainly macrobiotic form of the diet she followed was difficult to stick to and that meals took some time to prepare. On the Japanese Diet these problems are eliminated because there is a much wider range of foods to choose from, and cooking techniques have been simplified.

One of the major benefits of the Japanese Diet – its slimming properties – is now believed to have an effect on breast cancer as well.

Being overweight is certainly a risk factor for breast cancer. Leading cancer consultant Chris Williams of Southampton University explains: "There is a clear link with obesity. What you find is that an overweight woman produces more hormones because the fatty tissues themselves are able to produce hormones."

So losing excess fat on the Japanese Diet could do more than just help you get into that size 10 dress.

As an extra precaution in the fight against breast cancer, doctors strongly recommend that you check your breasts regularly for lumps – you can be shown how at your local well woman clinic. And please, please don't be frightened to check in case you find something. Ninety per cent of all breast lumps turn out to be nothing to worry about. Having a lump in your breast doesn't mean you've got a cancer. Nine times out of ten a lump will be completely benign and non-cancerous. So if you have got a lump you don't have to be afraid to go to the doctor – nearly all the time it will turn out to be a false alarm. On the rare occasions when it isn't a false alarm, spotting it early makes recovery much more likely.

Overall it appears that the Japanese Diet attacks the risks of breast cancer in several ways:

1. It is low in meat which is linked with increased risk of breast cancer.
2. It is low in the types of fat which may contribute to breast cancer.
3. It is rich in fresh vegetables and fruit which protect against breast cancer.
4. It decreases obesity which has a clear connection with breast cancer.

The Japanese Diet and Other Cancers

About one in three people in the UK develop cancer at some time in their lives, and according to current figures, a quarter of this country's population eventually die from it.

Although there are more than 200 different kinds of cancer which can occur in almost any part of the body, just four of them account for more than half of all cancer deaths: lung cancer; breast cancer (female); prostate cancer (male); and bowel cancer. Experts know how to prevent lung cancer – more than 90 per cent of lung cancer cases are caused purely by tobacco smoking.

That leaves the other three – breast, prostate and bowel. Rates of all these cancers are comparatively low in Japan, and researchers strongly believe that this is due to factors in the Japanese way of eating.

> **In the UK in 1994 there were 139,712 deaths from cancer (72,835 men and 66,877 women)**

Most cancer experts are now pretty sure that diet plays an important role in the development of many cancers, to the extent that they think perhaps a third of all cancer deaths could be prevented by changes in diet.

The biggest and most important research study into cancer this century is the EPIC (European Prospective Investigation into Cancer) project. Launched in 1992, this massive study of the link between diet and cancer will study a quarter of a million Europeans for at least twenty years. Already EPIC scientists are predicting that a diet rich in raw or lightly cooked fresh vegetables and fresh fish will be found to decrease cancer rates by as much as 80 per cent. Many scientists are openly recommending that the sort of eating represented by Japanese Diet is exactly what will prove to be most beneficial.

Dr Elio Riboli, EPIC's international co-ordinator, has said: "Diet is believed to be involved in several of the most common cancers and after tobacco it is likely to be one of the major contributing elements to the occurrence of cancer. So far, however, our knowledge is limited to the beneficial effects of a diet rich in fruit, vegetables and cereals, while the role of other important dietary components is still unclear."

EPIC predictions of possible cancer prevention through diet

Cancer	Proportion preventable through diet	Number preventable	Proportion of total cancer death preventable
Large bowel	90 per cent	15,153	10 per cent
Stomach	90 per cent	8,156	6 per cent
Pancreas	50 per cent	3,058	2 per cent
Breast	50 per cent	7,004	5 per cent
Oesophagus	20 per cent	1,002	1 per cent
Bladder	20 per cent	950	1 per cent
Lung	20 per cent	6,916	5 per cent
Prostate	10 per cent	785	1 per cent

Dr Tim Key of the Imperial Cancer Research Fund is working on the Oxford University end of the EPIC collaboration. He explains: "We are looking at the five commonest cancers in Britain: lung, stomach, bowel, breast and prostate. It won't be until around the year 2,000 that we start getting some firm results, but there is already a lot of work around that suggests we should get some positive links between the digestive cancers [bowel and stomach] and diet.

"For example, about 30 different studies have already pointed towards a diet high in vegetables and fruit as being connected with lower rates of cancer, but we don't yet know quite how it works."

Leading cancer researcher Professor Karol Sikora agrees: "I am personally convinced that there is a dietary component in the development of cancers. There is a lot of epidemiological evidence (gained from studying large groups of people) that seems to suggest the importance of a high fresh food intake in protecting against cancer."

Professor Sikora believes that eating the Japanese way is close to an ideal cancer preventative diet for breast and bowel cancer. Now he and other researchers are trying to find out exactly what it is about a diet like the Japanese Diet that has this protective effect.

Tim Key reports: "There definitely appears to be a protective element in eating plenty of fresh vegetables and fruit. The next question is what is it about these fruit and vegetables – vitamins, which vitamins? We don't know exactly how it works yet."

Writing in the respected medical journal, *The Lancet*, in January 1995, Tufts University of Boston researcher Mohsen Meydani suggests that vitamin E is particularly important. He writes: "The most widely accepted biological function of vitamin E is its anti-oxidant property, protecting cellular structures against damage from oxygen-free radicals. Several experimental and epidemiological studies suggest that vitamin E might reduce the risk of cancer. Though apparent vitamin E deficiency is rare, marginal deficiency may exist in large numbers of the population."

Vitamin E occurs especially in soya beans and sunflower seeds – both important parts of the Japanese Diet.

Professor Sikora believes that another vitamin, vitamin A, is important particularly in its early form, called beta-carotene. He explains: "We know the body has cancer preventatives which supply restorers to mend the damage in DNA linked with cancer. We think beta-carotene is one of these."

As we discover more about how eating the Japanese way may help prevent cancers, the outlook for overcoming the disease is beginning to look more positive. The current estimate is that more than 80 per cent of cancers may be avoidable through changes in diet, lifestyle, behaviour and environment, and the World Health Organisation has commented: "It would seem that the majority of human cancer is potentially avoidable." In its report, *Diet, Nutrition and the Prevention of Chronic Diseases*, the WHO comes out in favour of a Japanese style of eating.

Hugh Faulkner, author of *Against All Odds*, puts down his remission from prostate cancer to the Japanese-style macrobiotic diet he ate, writing: "After two or three weeks on the diet I began to feel much better and more energetic than I had for years."

Bowel cancer is the third most common of all the cancers in this country (excluding skin cancers, which are rarely fatal) with nearly 31,000 new cases every year in the UK.

Dr Tim Key of the EPIC study says: "The diet link is intuitively obvious when it comes to bowel and stomach cancers, in fact, for bowel cancer no other major cause has yet been suggested apart from diet."

In this case high fibre in the diet seems to be the important factor. So far about twenty-two studies have been carried out into the protective effect of a high-fibre diet, and eleven of these showed a reduction in risk among those with a high-fibre diet as compared with a low-fibre one.

Doctors are concerned that because Westerners move their bowels comparatively infrequently, with low amounts of bulk, this means that carcinogenic chemicals in waste product have a chance to stay in the bowel for longer.

This long contact time with the bowel wall gives the carcinogens a chance to be absorbed into the cells. In Africa, where the people have large, soft, frequent bowel motions (about three times more than the average Westerner), cancer of the large bowel is virtually non-existent. In Japan too, rice, pulses and vegetables provide the high levels of fibre needed in a healthy diet.

The one question mark over the Japanese way of eating is

the relatively high rates of stomach cancer (not a major cancer world-wide) which exist in Japan. At the moment there are various theories as to why this should be so. One view is that an infection, H.Pylori, may be the cause. This infection has already been found to be associated with stomach cancer in studies conducted in the UK and some researchers think it may be widespread in Japan. Another theory is that the Japanese method of smoking fish may be to blame. Just in case this does turn out to be the reason, you will find that Japanese smoked and cured fish are not used in the recipes in this book. Where smoked fish is used – which is very rarely – British smoked salmon is substituted. Another similar theory is that high levels of salt intake may be a feature, and because of the amount of seaweed, seafood and salty sauces the Japanese eat this may be a factor. To counteract this, there are none of the more salty Japanese recipes in this diet, and salt is not used for seasoning. Nor should you add salt when cooking rice, pasta or vegetables.

Overall though, the Japanese Diet is clearly linked with cancer prevention in several important ways:

1. High levels of fibre in the diet protect against bowel cancer.
2. Vitamin E, present in soya beans, has been shown to decrease risks of prostate cancer especially.
3. General high levels of anti-oxidant vitamins present in fresh vegetables and fruit are thought to protect against cancers generally.

The Japanese Diet and Heart Disease

At a time when most British men (and older women too) are increasingly worried about their risks of coronary heart disease it is wonderful news to discover that by switching to the Japanese Diet it is possible your chances of developing heart disease will drop rapidly.

For every hundred British men who are hit by heart disease, only four Japanese males will get the disease. Overall, Japanese rates of heart disease are the lowest in the affluent world. Better still, as rates of heart disease world-wide fall, Japanese figures are getting even lower. In Japan the death rate from coronary heart disease fell by 32 per cent between 1979 and 1989.

> # Coronary heart disease hits 96 per cent fewer men in Japan than in Britain

Naturally the world's leading medical researchers have responded to these encouraging statistics by studying the Japanese way of life closely in order to discover just what there is about it that protects Japanese people from getting heart disease.

Is it the nature of the Japanese race, scientists asked, or is it something about the way they live and eat, that is helping them to be so healthy? Very quickly researchers discovered that it was nothing to do with just being Japanese. They looked at groups of Japanese who had moved to America and found that once these immigrant Japanese took up the American way of life, they were just as prone to heart disease as born and bred Americans. Most scientists now firmly believe that it is the Japanese way of eating which so greatly decreases their risk of heart disease. But there are still many theories on exactly why this should be so. Some researchers believe high levels of fish oils in the diet are what count, while others have pointed to the amount of soya eaten in the form of soya beans, soya bean curd, soy sauce etc. The trouble is that no one really knows exactly what causes the heart disease process to begin. Researchers have identified various common factors shared by those who get heart disease, and they call these risk factors. People in the medical world agree about the risk factors for heart disease, even though they don't agree about what the disease really is. That means they can spot the signs that someone may develop the process of heart disease even though they still aren't quite sure what triggers the process in the first place. Here is a brief guide to the common risk factors:

What is Heart Disease?

The precise medical term for heart disease is Coronary Heart Disease (often shortened to CHD). When discussing heart disease, doctors are talking about the range of cardio-vascular (literally heart/blood vessel) illnesses which people loosely refer to as "heart attack"; "heart trouble"; "coronary disease"; "coronary artery disease"; "coronary thrombosis" etc.

How does Heart Disease Happen?

Heart disease is actually a long process of events, which happens in two stages.

STAGE ONE

This is the long-term narrowing up of the arteries with sticky deposits of calcium, cholesterol and fibrinogen called plaques. This goes on for twenty or thirty years making the artery smaller and is what people tend to call "hardening of the arteries".

This seems to happen to a greater or lesser extent to everyone and scientists have not yet agreed on exactly what causes it to happen.

STAGE TWO

On its own stage one is not too dangerous, but the second element of the process is what causes problems. When the artery walls are roughened by the plaque deposits, the body is fooled into thinking that the artery wall has been ruptured in some way, so the blood clotting system goes into action and covers the rough spot with a blood clot. (There is national variation in how easily blood clots. In Britain our blood tends to clot rather easily.) Either the clot can stay where it is, narrowing the artery still further, or it can break off and float away in the blood stream to become lodged somewhere else where it will cause problems – especially heart attack.

Heart Attack

Heart attack is usually triggered when a fairly large clot has formed and then moved on to relodge and block the vessel leading into the heart. The medical term for this is coronary thrombosis. It causes the blood supply to the heart muscle to be blocked off completely, starving the muscle of oxygen and leaving it unable to keep the heart pumping.

Angina

Some people suffer long-term problems when the supply of blood is only partly blocked off. This means that although the heart manages all right most of the time, when it is working hard it can't get all the oxygen it needs, causing the chest pains we call angina. Most heart attack and angina sufferers are taken by surprise when the illness strikes, but in fact it doesn't come about suddenly at all.

1. Age

This is the first and most obvious risk factor to have been identified: most people who get heart disease are in middle age or older. It is extremely rare in young people. As Dr John Brown of the Flora Project points out, there is an obvious reason for this: "Laying down of plaque deposits is a long-term process. It can go on for twenty or thirty years gradually making the artery smaller before the symptoms are actually felt."

If the laying down of plaque deposits can be slowed down, then this will help postpone heart disease. Scientists looking at Japanese nutrition believe that this may be happening with Japanese men because of the large amount of fish they eat. Fish is high in oils including essential fatty acids (known as EFAs) which improve the health and functioning of the vascular system. It is believed that fish oils promote the formation of a group of hormones (called prostaglandins) which help prevent blood clots in the circulatory system and reduce the amount of fat circulating in the blood.

2. Being Male

Up to the age of sixty-five men are three times more likely than women to suffer heart disease. This is why it has tended to be thought of as a "men's disease". In fact, after the age of sixty-five a woman's chances of getting heart disease actually increase more rapidly than men's. By the age of eighty-five the two sexes have pretty much equal risks – although the overall death rate for women remains consistently lower at every age group.

The reason for this is that the female hormone oestrogen protects women from heart disease, up until the menopause, when supply of the hormone stops. Studying why this should be has given researchers a big insight into the process at work with heart disease. They have found that oestrogen changes the type of cholesterol circulating in the blood. One type of cholesterol, low density lipoprotein (LDL), is the culprit when it comes to forming plaque deposits. While another type, high density lipoprotein (HDL), is completely blameless, continuing to circulate freely in the blood and not laying down plaque deposits. Female oestrogen sends the body signals to give priority to the formation of HDL cholesterol and forget about making LDL.

When scientists studied soya bean products (a major part of Japanese cuisine) to discover why they might have a similar protective effect to female oestrogen hormones, they discovered that they contained a plant hormone called "phytoestrogen" which behaves very much like female oestrogen.

Japanese eating can encourage the formation of "good" HDL cholesterol

---

Their study gave extra corroboration for the oestrogen/anti-LDL cholesterol link when it discovered that a soya-rich diet — like the Japanese diet — tended to lower LDL cholesterol and increase HDL cholesterol in just the way that female hormones do.

3. Family History

If other members of your family have also suffered from heart disease your own risk can increase by as much as four times. At first scientists thought this might suggest a genetic, inherited element in heart disease, but apart from one very rare illness which causes the sufferer to put down massive amounts of cholesterol no matter what they do, no genetic basis for heart disease has been found. Which means there must be something else at work, connected with family background. Most researchers have now decided that a family's lifestyle and eating habits through the generations are what count.

4. Faulty Diet

Study after study has shown that heart disease is in some way linked with faulty diet. Yet it has been much more difficult for scientists to pin down exactly what elements of a diet give risk of or protection from heart disease.

For a long time it has been stressed that high levels of saturated fat (fat from animals and dairy) in the diet promote high cholesterol and in turn heart disease. But as more and more scientists tested this theory they found exceptions and drawbacks. Most now accept that although the link is there, it is nothing like as simple as we thought.

Some scientists, encouraged by the discoveries of the different effects of LDL and HDL cholesterol and how hormones could alter them, began to look at the role of the two different cholesterols in much more detail. In particular they wanted to find out exactly how what you ate could affect these different cholesterols.

Professor Michael Oliver of the Royal Brompton National Heart and Lung Institute was unconvinced by various trials on reducing total and saturated fats for the prevention of coronary heart disease. So instead he looked at what was actually happening to the cholesterol in the body. He agrees with other scientists that what really does the damage in heart disease is not cholesterol per se, but the part of the cholesterol that is linked to LDL. Why though, he asked himself, is LDL cholesterol a problem? He concluded that it is what happens to the LDL during bodily processes which causes it to lay down plaques, and the process he singled out is that of oxidation. Oxidation is a very common bio-chemical reaction which takes place all around us in life. It occurs when oxygen reacts with another material and breaks it down, causing waste products. An example of oxidation which takes place outside the body is when the oxygen in water (H_2O) comes into contact with iron and breaks it down, causing rust as a by-product.

The Japanese Diet helps reduce the process of oxidation of LDL cholesterol

---

Many scientists now believe that something like that is happening to the LDL cholesterol in our blood, so that when it comes into contact with oxygen it is broken down and waste products (they are called oxygen-free radicals) are produced.

For example leading researcher Dr Robert Youngson believes that it is only when LDL cholesterol becomes oxidised that it starts to trigger the foundation of the plaques in the artery that lead to heart disease. This may be because the chemical change brought about by oxidation triggers the body's immune system into action, leading to damage to blood vessels and clot formation. This theory could turn out to be a breakthrough in the fight against heart disease, since it explains why diet has such a complicated impact on our risk of the disease.

It appears that eating fat is dangerous only if the oxidation process occurs – and the oxidation process can be overcome. Once again the Japanese Diet turns out to have the answer. By including large quantities of the vitamins A, C and E present in fresh vegetables and fruit – which prevent the oxidation process – the Japanese Diet neutralises potential harmful effects of fat and LDL cholesterol.

Dr Robert Youngson reports: "A survey of 11,000 men in 12 countries found that for those with low levels of these vitamins the death rates from heart attack were higher than in those with higher levels. This was not a marginal difference."

Two of the world's leading researchers into heart disease, Sir Richard Doll and Professor Richard Peto of Oxford University, have such high hopes for these theories that they are directing their Heart Protection Study Group in a major investigation which started in 1994 and will continue for at least five years. More support for the oxidation theory had come from the study of the effect of smoking on heart disease risks. It has been shown that a smoker is three times more likely to suffer heart disease than a non-smoker. And once again oxidation is likely to be at the root of the problem. It is well known that the pollutant effect of cigarette smoking causes oxidation elsewhere in the body (one reason why smokers tend to have poor complexions) and it now seems likely that smoking promotes oxidation of LDL cholesterol.

5. Obesity

One other risk factor for heart disease is being overweight. Being overweight is associated with other syndromes such as high blood pressure, raised cholesterol levels and physical inactivity. This means that if you are overweight you are at higher risk of heart disease than if you were of a desirable weight. This is another area where the Japanese Diet can help, since it promotes weight loss and helps to keep already slim people in shape.

So as scientists research the Japanese way of eating, it appears that the Japanese Diet attacks the risks and causes of heart disease in many different ways:

1. It is low in saturated fat which therefore helps reduce obesity and the potential laying down of LDL cholesterol.
2. It includes soya which mimics female hormones, helping prevent the formation of harmful LDL cholesterol.
3. It is rich in A, C and E vitamins from fresh vegetables and fruit which prevent the oxidation of LDL cholesterol.
4. It is high in essential fatty acids and fish oils which prevent formation of blood clots.

The Japanese Diet and General Health

Sir Richard Doll, the man who proved the link between smoking and lung cancer, and who is perhaps the most highly respected epidemiological health researcher of the century, gave a speech in 1982 in which he concluded that to avoid the major diseases of the Western world: "cancer, coronary heart disease, hypertension [high blood pressure], diabetes, diverticular disease [a bowel disease], duodenal ulcer or constipation" diet is an important factor. The type of diet he advocated in his speech is

○ high in cereals (like rice)
○ high in fresh vegetables and fruit
○ stresses fish and poultry protein rather than red meats
○ has a low proportion of hard fats
○ includes few dairy products, or eggs
○ has little refined sugar

That recommendation is an excellent description of the Japanese Diet.

Had Professor Doll been speaking solely about Oriental styles of

24

eating he could have added even more health benefits to his list. For example, the Japanese have low rates of arthritis.

Many researchers think that the lack of possible toxins and inflammatories in Japanese food may be why their arthritis rates are low. Certainly in Britain studies have shown that arthritis improved when extract of green-lipped mussel was taken, a shellfish from the waters surrounding Japan and New Zealand and an important ingredient in Japanese cooking.

Nor is osteoporosis (brittle bone disease) a particular problem in Japan, even though the low intake of calcium-providing dairy products might suggest that it could be. In fact calcium is present in lots of Japanese ingredients – especially fish, beans and vegetables. The soya bean has also been found to have an additional anti-osteoporotic effect.

What surprises many people who eat Japanese-style is how much you can eat while still losing weight (if overweight) or maintaining a stable weight (if correct weight). This is a common feature of Oriental eating habits. For example, Chinese people have been found to consume 20 per cent more calories than Americans, despite remaining thinner throughout their lives. The Chinese lead far less sedentary lives than Americans which is an important factor in this equation. But in Japan the picture is very similar – despite the fact that as a developed nation, the Japanese are almost as sedentary as the Americans.

Researchers believe that the actual amount of calories consumed when eating Japanese-style becomes relatively unimportant, since the quality of nutrition is so high. Of course this is wonderful news for slimmers who long to be free from the tyranny of calorie counting.

In general Japanese food is delicate and refined, making it ideal for healthy eating. It majors on fresh, clean, natural tastes and ingredients. Hot, spicy flavourings and artificial, ingredients are not much used in Japanese cooking. This means that it has few of the health drawbacks of the typical Western diet high in junk food.

This concentration on fresh food, on raw vegetables and on whole foods means the diet is high in important vitamins, micro-nutrients and fibre as well as being low in saturated fats and additives. It is widely believed that this is the reason why bowel diseases are rare in Japan and why Japanese people tend to live into a healthy old age.

From a general health point of view it is key to the Japanese attitude to food that the appearance should satisfy the eye as much as the flavours satisfy the palate. This is a great plus for slimmers since it encourages slow eating while food is savoured and increases a general feeling of satisfaction without actually increasing the amount eaten.

Japanese food is usually served very lightly cooked, and vegetables and salads are often presented raw. Because cooking time is very short, especially with table-prepared meals, it means that the essential nutrients present in the ingredients are not destroyed as can be the case with traditional British cooking methods.

Apart from this overall healthy approach to cooking, the major ingredients of Japanese eating are also individually extremely rich in health-giving factors.

The idea of getting health-giving nutrients through diet rather than supplementation is important, because unless very carefully handled by more expert nutritionists than we are, imbalances can occur. If one nutrient (for example, vitamins A and E) is taken to excess, antagonistic reactions can occur which means that the supplement may end up working against the body's best interests.

Macrobiotic practitioners – who follow a more severe and restricted version of Japanese-style eating – believe very strongly that the diet works in a positive way to answer the body's needs. Practitioner Simon Brown writes that in a period of only four to six weeks: "The initial improvements a macrobiotic counsellor will be looking for are an increase in energy, a full night's sleep, a good appetite, regular bowel movements, greater concentration, and greater emotional stability."

The health possibilities of Japanese-style eating habits were first recognised by their own doctors in the last century. A Japanese army doctor named Sagen Ishizuka noticed how much his soldier patients improved when he insisted that they were provided with traditional Japanese foods, rather than the debased version supplied by army rations.

Later another Japanese, George Ohsawa, researched these findings further and his discoveries led him to develop a special version of traditional Japanese-style eating which he called a macrobiotic diet. Many people still use Ohsawa's macrobiotic diet, but it has not become widely popular because it can be restrictive and difficult to follow. Nor does it include all the foods that would be eaten in a typical Japanese diet.

Nevertheless from the 1970s onwards medical researchers all over the world began to look more closely at Japanese eating habits to discover why the Japanese suffer so little from the diseases shared by the rest of the affluent world – especially heart disease and some cancers.

The World Health Organisation reached the conclusion that the high fibre and low saturated fat levels in their diet were associated with the low Japanese susceptibility to our major diseases. Later surveys linked the high proportions of fish oils in the diet to protection from heart disease, a theory endorsed by epidemiologist Dr Peter Elwood (the man who helped prove that aspirin helps recovery from heart disease) and America's Professor Geoffrey Blumberg (a leading authority on age-related disease).

Mass survey after mass survey has shown that the Japanese Diet is the healthiest in the world. It protects against heart disease and several forms of cancer. It keeps you slim, fit and young. Moreover, it is one of the simplest and easiest eating regimes to adopt. Unlike so many restrictive diets that have been proved not to work, the Japanese diet is just a matter of incorporating a few key foods such as fatty fish, soya and rice into your diet.

All round, the Japanese Diet offers a number of health benefits for men and women alike:

1. It is high in fibre to promote healthy bowel activity.
2. It reduces the inflammation present in arthritis.
3. It contains high levels of soya, a protective against heart disease, cancer and osteoporosis.

4. It is effective in weight control.
5. It is high in the fresh vegetables recommended by medical experts.
6. It is a light way of eating which promotes good digestion.

For the first time in *The Japanese Diet* the simple, typical Japanese way of eating is described – easy to stick to; simple to follow; enjoyable to eat; and a proven all-round health promoter

For further information on sources and research quoted in this chapter, see Bibliography of Sources and References, page 235.

2

TAKING A WHOLE NEW ANGLE ON DIETING

By now I'm sure you'll have guessed that with the Japanese Diet you are about to experience something new. For a start, it sounds more like fun than a diet – and whoever heard of a diet where you could have fried rice, soy sauce and even Chinese take-away!

The Japanese Diet is bound to strike you as different for a number of reasons. It first attracted the attention of health researchers and writers like me because of its disease combating properties; its slimming effects are really only a side effect. I think this makes it a diet you can really trust because you know it is making you slimmer by making you healthier.

Of course, for researchers, the most interesting thing about the Japanese Diet is that it has been tried and tested by a whole nation – the Japanese – who have been following it for centuries! And this means that it really is a diet for life. Most slimming diets which talk about lifelong weight control mean one of two things: either you must stick to the particular restrictive slimming diet advocated for the rest of your life; or you will have to go on a series of slimming diets throughout your life, with periods of unrestricted (possibly binge) eating in between.

The first alternative is simply unrealistic. Most ordinary slimming diets are far too limited to be followed for a lifetime. It would be impossibly boring, intrusive into daily life and even nutritionally dangerous. The second alternative is usually called "yo-yo" dieting and has now been clinically proven to be a risk factor for heart disease, as well as other health and emotional problems.

The Japanese Diet is a diet for life because it is not in fact a conventional slimming diet at all, it is a national cuisine. I suppose I should really have called this book the Japanese diet, with a small d, because it is about the traditional diet of the Japanese people. The Japanese wouldn't have any difficulty sticking to the Japanese Diet permanently, because it is already what they eat every day. You could say the Japanese are already on the Japanese Diet for life – and we know how slim and healthy it keeps them.

It is perhaps just our bad luck that the average twentieth-century American-English cuisine happens not to be especially slimming or healthy. It can be, of course. We all know people who stay slim seemingly without effort but who claim never to diet. This is because luckily for them, the type of food they enjoy eating from day to day happens to be healthy and non-fattening. To those of us struggling to stay slim, those people's "normal diet" with a small d would seem like A Diet.

That is the real problem with Diets. They need to be slimming and healthy but at the same time flexible and varied enough to become a more or less unconscious part of life. Sure, even the healthiest of us over-eats or eats junk sometimes, but by and large a good diet needs to be followed the majority of the time, not just as an isolated outbreak of The Diet.

So how can we turn The Diet into our diet? The very committed and strong-willed sometimes achieve it by re-learning nutrition and re-thinking their Western-style eating from scratch. But it is hard to do that if you are still staying within basically the same cuisine, with all its reminders of the tempting foods available. One of the strengths of the Japanese Diet is that it takes you into a completely new way of eating, with a new outlook on food altogether.

This makes it much easier to abandon old bad eating habits completely as you get totally absorbed in discovering a whole new cuisine – and the way of life that goes with it.

Being introduced to this new way of thinking is terribly important to the long-term success of your diet. Psychiatrists researching the field of dieting, overweight and eating disorders have discovered that someone's mental approach and emotional attitude towards food is at least as important as their actual food intake.

Food, they argue, is about emotional fulfilment, comfort and psychological needs as much as it is about your body's physical requirement for calories. I don't think anyone who has ever sat down to that mid-morning cup of fresh coffee and a buttery croissant or reached for another chocolate as they watch their favourite film would disagree with that. The scientists conclude from this that going on a Diet, denying ourselves the fulfilment of all these needs, is also a psychological step. When we go on a Diet, we tend to be looking to it to answer all sorts of problems, not just overweight. We look to a Diet to make us happier, prettier, more successful either at work or with the opposite sex; to make us feel better in some abstract and usually not consciously defined way.

Proof of this comes from the fact that a quarter of the women in Britain who go on a Diet from time to time are not clinically overweight at all. Subconsciously, or even sometimes consciously, they know this perfectly well and frankly don't really expect to lose any more than a temporary couple of pounds. Indeed if they did manage to lose any more they would become underweight, and here we are entering the field of anorexia. No, what these people want (and I freely admit that this has at times included myself) is something to make themselves feel better.

I believe that one of the real root reasons for going on a Diet is to try to feel better about yourself; to like yourself better.

Think about it for a moment. Here is the statement you start out with: "I am going on a diet because I feel fat and horrible and I want to be thin." Here is the statement you end up with: "I am going on a diet because I don't like how I am at the moment, and I want to be able to like myself more." Ask yourself in your heart of hearts which is the truer statement.

I admit that for me, and for most of my readers over the years, first as Woman's Editor of the *Daily Express* and now as a health writer, the second statement is the one that really hits the nail on the head.

Yet few conventional slimming diets ever acknowledge this. They simply make more or less unrealistic nutritional demands without ever addressing the inner you that really needs help and encouragement.

This is where the Japanese Diet is so special. By being based on a genuine national cuisine rather than an artificial "Diet", the Japanese Diet reflects an entire culture and offers a real insight into a very different approach to life.

The Japanese, and indeed the entire Oriental, outlook on food is that it is one element in a whole syndrome of experiences which contribute towards health, happiness and well-being. They have an extremely holistic attitude which says that what we eat and how we eat it is intermeshed with a range of activities including exercise, meditation, relaxation and sensory pleasure. All these things together have a role in nourishing our inner selves, just as much as our physical outer bodies.

That is why Japanese food is served with such care and delicacy, and why traditions like the tea ceremony (see pages 184–5) are so important. The Japanese are recognising, in a way that we often fail to do in the West, that we need to care for ourselves and that eating and drinking is one way of doing it.

So the Japanese Diet, unlike almost any other conventional Diet I can think of, does not begin from a starting point of denial. It doesn't deny your need to get pleasure, entertainment and comfort from food. It doesn't deny that food is one of the ways we comfort the inner self. Instead the Japanese Diet accepts. It accepts that you will need your Diet to fulfil far more wide ranging, and deeper, goals than just getting thinner. It accepts that you need to care for yourself. And stemming from this standpoint of acceptance rather than denial, I hope that you will achieve the goal of self-acceptance while you are following the Japanese Diet.

Self-acceptance is an important aspect of Buddhist philosophy. Qualities valued in Buddhism include spontaneity, following your instincts and the simple expression of joy. All these attributes are signs that someone has gained not only self-knowledge, but the wisdom to accept themselves as they are – warts and all.

Self-acceptance doesn't mean that you stop wanting to change and improve yourself. But it does mean losing all the negative feelings of guilt and self-blame that are so often attached to the desire for self-improvement.

Take the slimmer who is genuinely overweight. He may well go through the first four weeks of this diet without losing much fat, but if he learns self-acceptance then he is on the road to success. Then he can say to himself, "Yes, I still need to lose weight for health reasons in order to reduce my risk of heart disease and other health problems," but he can now come to his weight loss regime with a completely positive approach, without the horrible undermining poison of self-hatred, blame, guilt and defeatism.

Even more fortunate is the slimmer who is not genuinely overweight. I sincerely hope that after the first four weeks of this diet she hasn't lost any weight at all. What I think she will have gained is the understanding to realise that her need to diet is not about weight at all, but reflects stresses and dissatisfactions in other areas of her life. What she can now do is re-read the latter parts of this book and start having a good think about the positive things that already exist in her life (like the fact that she doesn't need to slim) and what she can do to change the less satisfactory things. That is why the Japanese-style Diet is a diet for life, in every sense of the phrase.

Most of us will not want to adopt total Japanese eating permanently, and once you have learnt about nutrition from following the diet you won't need to. Instead you can adapt the health-giving aspects of Japanese eating to make your day-to-day Western cooking healthier and less fattening.

Once you have finished reading this book, and are ready to commence the diet, I hope you will already be approaching dieting from a completely new angle. By the time you finish the Japanese Diet I think you will also have a new attitude to your whole life.

3

FOLLOWING THE DIET

As you will have realised, the Japanese Diet is about far more than just losing weight. Whether you are young or old, male or female, overweight or underweight, the Japanese Diet has something to offer you. Especially if you are feeling under the weather, fatigued, have a long-term illness or have recently recovered from illness, the Japanese Diet is a wonderful tonic and booster to the immune system.

If you are worried about such ailments of modern times as heart disease and cancer, the Japanese Diet is definitely for you. But even if none of these things concerns you, I am sure you will enjoy the new look at life and the adventure into a new culinary culture which you will find on the Japanese Diet.

It is not necessary to stick closely to the diet if all you are looking for is a bit of a change and some advice on healthy eating to boost your immune system. I'm sure that many people reading this book will simply use it as a cookery book or an interesting insight into a culture very different from our own.

However, to get the full health and slimming benefits of the Japanese Diet, you need to stick to it very closely. For the next four weeks at least you will need to take on board a whole new attitude to food. If you can make that changed attitude a permanent part of your outlook, then you will certainly be able to look forward to a life of good health and no weight problems.

But like all things that are worth doing, it won't be all plain sailing. Chocolates, cakes, endless cups of coffee, burgers and pizzas – all the junk that we Westerners consume without thinking – will disappear completely from your diet. Traditional Japanese simply don't eat them – and that is one of the major reasons for their slimness and long lives. Eating a Japanese lunch and dinner will not do you any good if you have been browsing on biscuits and coffee all day long. If you really want to let the Japanese Diet change your life, then you must give up Western high-sugar, high-caffeine, high-fat foods. If you don't really care enough about it to make that sacrifice, if only for four weeks, then fine – but accept that while you will have fun trying new recipes you will still remain essentially the same in terms of your health and weight. Sorry about that, but you have to face it now.

The good news is that the Japanese Diet is such fun and so interesting that you will find it easier to give up bad food habits than at any other time in your life. To help you along, there are tips on how to substitute other foods, and what to do if a craving strikes (see page 39).

If you read the book carefully you will also discover lots of other ways of fulfilling yourself and feeling good which don't involve food at all. And you could very well change your whole life by learning how to replace food as a source of comfort, and growing to the point where you are your own best friend, rather than a bar of Cadbury's Dairy Milk.

This section tells you how to follow the Japanese Diet. Read it carefully, and try to put it into practice.

Step one

Read the whole book through to the end before you start the diet. It is always very tempting to skip the bits that don't look as if they are relevant to slimming. In fact the Japanese Diet stresses that for a slimming diet to be successful, it must be about much more than just food. So there are sections about feeling good and looking good which will help you greatly even before you start the diet. Reading these sections now

will help you a lot if you reach a crisis while you are on
the diet.

Step two

If you are following the Japanese Diet for slimming purposes,
measure and/or weigh yourself and note the starting statistics in
your diary – but do remember it is important to rely on more
than just your weight to measure how well you are doing. Weight
can fluctuate for a number of reasons. Most women gain weight in
the ten days before their period due to water retention. If you are
starting a fitness programme you may notice that you actually gain
weight. This is because muscle weighs more than fat (even though
it is less bulky), so if you increase the proportion of your body
which is muscle and decrease the proportion which is fat, you will
gain weight while actually measuring less.

Those who don't want to lose weight (or more accurately,
fat) will not be concerned at their starting measurements. But
everybody should note down their goals before starting the diet,
whatever the goals are. It is worth spending a little time thinking
about this. Business experts tell us that goals should be clearly
defined, worthwhile, measurable and above all achievable. If you
think carefully about why you are starting a diet you may find
that your goal isn't particularly clearly defined nor measurable, and
certainly not realistically achievable.

Very often a young woman starts a diet because she wants to
look like the models in a fashion magazine. As a goal this fails on
many counts:

○ **Is it clearly defined?** No, because what exactly does looking
   like a model mean? The minimum height for a fashion model
   is 5' 8''. The average British woman is 5' 4''. So does the goal
   include being four inches taller? The average price of one outfit
   photographed in a fashion magazine is £500–£1,000, more than
   the average British woman spends on clothes in an entire year.
   The goal needs to be much more precise.
○ **Is it worthwhile?** Not really; after all what is to be gained by

looking like a fashion model? The average fashion model is aged eighteen, unmarried, with few qualifications, works more than ten hours a day during sessions and has a career expectancy of only about six to ten years.

O **Is it measurable?** Not at all, unless you actually become a fashion model at the end of the diet.
O **Is it achievable?** No. You can't get taller, or younger, or richer, or happier, or change your bone structure by dieting. If a few more slimmers realised this at the outset there would be fewer disappointed people.

So set your goals carefully and be tough with yourself in asking what you really want out of this diet and whether it is honestly practical to expect to achieve it. Some examples of sensible, achievable goals are:

O I want to be an inch slimmer round my thighs.
O I want to improve my digestion.
O I want to have more energy during the day.
O I want to learn some new recipes.
O I want to improve my skin tone.
O I want a new interest.
O I want to learn about nutrition and its links with health.

Step three
Go shopping. This is one of the really fun parts of the Japanese Diet. You can have an adventurous trip to your local Chinatown. You can get yourself some lovely new beauty products to cheer yourself up when that Cadbury's Dairy Milk seems an awfully long way away. And the weekly trek round the supermarket is never going to be the same again once you find the corner with all the strange Oriental names.

At first you may notice yourself spending a little more on your week's shop than previously. This is mainly because you are stocking up your larder with items that will last for months. Also the quality of some of the ingredients is higher than things you may have been buying previously. Don't feel guilty about this.

Invest in yourself, you're worth it. For a list of Oriental stores in your area, see pages 45–9.

Step four

Follow the diet closely for four weeks. Daily menu plans and weekly shopping lists are given to enable you to do this easily. Halfway through, measure or weigh yourself. Don't do this any sooner as you may get a result that is falsely good or falsely bad. It takes your body time to re-adjust. Reassess your goals at this point to check whether they still seem right and whether they are achievable. Think about what you have learnt about yourself and your eating during this first fortnight and work out how to put that new knowledge to good use in the next two weeks. But don't be alarmed if you don't feel you have got very far. If a week is a short time in politics, in dieting it's a nanosecond.

Step five

At the end of the fourth week it is time for re-assessment. If you have been following the diet closely you will find you are already feeling healthier and less tired, and if you are trying to lose weight you will certainly have lost some. Those of us who just want to tone up a bit and lose a few pounds (probably no more than half a stone) will probably already be there. Those of us with a genuine weight issue (as opposed to a vanity problem) shouldn't expect to achieve our final goal in such a short space of time. The only lasting weight loss is a slow weight loss. Both groups need to realise that weight control is a matter of longterm lifestyle rather than a series of quick fixes. There is a great deal of information in this book about how to re-evaluate your lifestyle in order to achieve your goals, whether or not they are weight related. Now is the time to have a think about all these things. I hope you will want to incorporate permanently into your life at least some of the ideas – culinary and cultural – contained in this book, but ultimately only you can know what to do next.

Your Questions Answered

Are there any foods I am not allowed?

Unfortunately, yes. Here is a chart of what you will have to give up.

GIVE UP	SUBSTITUTE	CRAVING TIP
Added sugar	Should not be necessary	Some sugar is included in cooking, otherwise the foods to which we normally add sugar (eg, coffee, breakfast cereal) are not included in the diet
Added salt	Herbs, spice powder, soya sauce	Cravings for salty foods may indicate you have not enough savoury or protein items in your diet; try more fish dishes
Coffee	Green tea, fruit juice, water	If you get absolutely desperate, allow yourself only freshly brewed coffee; the time and effort of preparation makes it more satisfying and you are less likely to reach for a cup without thinking
Fizzy colas	Mineral water, fruit juice, vegetable juice, tomato juice	Have a wide choice of substitutes on hand to prevent boredom
Chocolate	Japanese nibbles, roasted nuts or seeds	Eat regular small, savoury meals to avoid the peaks and troughs of blood sugar levels which cause chocolate cravings
Cakes	Japanese snacks and nibbles	Use rice cakes topped with bean curd to create cake-like snacks
Bread	Rice crackers	Rice is the Japanese version of bread

What can I drink on the diet?

Moderate levels of alcohol are permitted on the diet. I suggest no more than seven units for a woman and fourteen for a man.

Unsweetened fruit juices, vegetable juice and tomato juice are allowed ad lib, as is water, mineral water and diluted pure lemon juice.

For hot drinks you can have hot broth/bouillon drinks or, like the Japanese, tea. Any Oriental tea is excellent, but Chinese and Japanese green tea especially is thought to be one of the main health-giving elements of the Japanese Diet. It is rich in anti-oxidants and mildly diuretic. Japanese green tea is available at Oriental stores and most major supermarket chains. If you are in London it is also worth checking out the Japanese Green Tea Bags by Wild Oats, 210 Westbourne Grove, London W11 (tel: 0171 229 1063) at £1.69 per pack.

Can I snack between meals?

There is one very simple rule on the Japanese Diet: drink when you are thirsty and eat when you are hungry. As long as you stick to the foods on the diet and don't start browsing on junk, then you can eat what you want, when you want. Most people eating three good meals a day find they have little appetite for between-meal snacks, but others prefer to nibble frequently rather than having main meals. Either is fine.

Will it fit into my working lunch times?

The recipes and menu plans all take into account the fact that most of us eat our lunch away from home. There are lots of tips about packed meals you can take to work for when you are following the diet closely at the beginning. Later, when you are more used to the ideas behind the Japanese Diet, you will probably be able to adapt canteen meals if you need to.

What about eating out or entertaining?

On the Japanese Diet this is positively recommended, so much so that there are whole sections of the book devoted to it. The idea is that this diet should be a fun, enhancing element in your life, not a period of purgatory. Try diet recipes on your friends when they come for dinner and defy them to realise they are eating healthy food.

Will the family like it?

This is primarily a diet for you as an individual. A lot of the philosophy behind the diet is about making time and space for yourself and your needs, rather than simply seeing yourself as the family provider. However, the food on the Japanese Diet is so exciting that you may find you have a family of eager dieters on your hands after all. If they are cautious about joining in, and you want them to participate, then try winning them over gradually with Western favourites like sukiyaki and beef teriyaki, which are all included in the recipe sections of the book (see pages 130 and 151). The Japanese Diet is perfectly safe for children and supplies all the nutrients they need, though you may want to add a little more dairy foods for children who are still growing.

4

WHERE TO BUY JAPANESE

SUPERMARKETS

Tesco

Of all the big supermarket chains, Tesco is definitely the one to choose for one-stop Japanese and Oriental shopping. Not only does it have excellent coverage, with branches all over the country, but it also has the most extraordinarily complete range of goods. In fact I think I can guarantee that at a Tesco main branch you will be able to get every single ingredient you need for the Japanese Diet – including really unusual things like nori seaweed and miso soup. Before you begin the diet, I would recommend paying a visit to your local Tesco and having a good nose around, buying whatever takes your fancy. Having an exciting new range of foods to choose from makes beginning a diet much more fun and interesting. Here are just a few of the special things you should look out for.

In the canned foods section you will find **water chestnuts**, various types of **mixed vegetables** for stir-frying, and **peeled chestnuts**. The canned food section will also have tinned soups and there are several kinds of Oriental **ready-made soups**, including vegetable and hot and sour, as well as **miso** (by Sanchi). In the packet soups section there are also some **dried noodles soups**. Also look out for **Knorr Soup of the World Japanese Noodle Soup**. There is a fantastic range of condiments, seasonings and sauces, which are usually kept close to the Western cooking sauces and oils section. These include **teriyaki barbecue sauce, classic Chinese marinade, Chinese five spice powder**, and **rice seasoning**. In the cereals and pulses section there is a big range of different kinds of noodles and rices to choose from. Specific purely Japanese specialities include **kombu, arame, wakame** and **nori** varieties of seaweed, all by the leading Japanese brand Sanchi, as well as Sanchi's own **hot and spicy wasabi** (Japanese horseradish) **chips** and **mugi brand miso soup mix**. Other brand names with good Oriental ranges to look out for include Schwartz, Sharwood's, Lawrys, Lotus and Amoy. For further information about Tesco, phone the head office in Waltham Cross on: 01992 632222.

Waitrose

With only 113 branches nationwide, concentrated mainly in the South-East of England, Waitrose is one of the less accessible of the major supermarket chains – which is a shame because it has a very good variety of Oriental foods. If you do have a branch within reasonable distance it is a good idea to go there as it is likely that you will be able to get all you need at one go.

Look on the speciality sauces and condiment shelves for: **Japanese soy sauce; light soy sauce; teriyaki sauce; chilli sauce; five spice soy sauce; hoisin sauce; plum sauce; fish sauce**.

The brand names to watch out for are Sharwood's (who have an enormous range of Oriental sauces and seasonings); Blue Dragon (an imported Oriental range); and Amoy (the best-known Oriental range).

In the fresh fruit and vegetable section you should be able to find fresh **root ginger, coriander, lemon grass** and **shiitake mushrooms**. Various versions of **bean curd** are stocked in both the long-life shelves and the prepared meal section. Some branches also stock **seaweed**.

For further information about Waitrose, phone the head office in Bracknell on: 01344 424680.

Safeway

Safeway has a conveniently large number of branches all over the country. However, there can be big differences in the exact range of stock carried by each individual store. If you are lucky enough to live near a large, urban branch, you will find a wide range of goods – and you've probably already discovered you hardly ever need to shop anywhere else! If, like me, your local Safeway is rather more restricted, you may have trouble getting hold of things like soya beans and shiitake mushrooms, but if you ask the branch manager, I'm sure they will order them for you.

Look in the vegetarian section for **Cauldron** brand **bean curd**. In the cooking oils section you will find a particularly nice own-brand of **toasted sesame oil**.

For further information about Safeway, phone the head office in Maidstone, Kent on: 01622 712000.

Sainsbury

With 355 stores nationwide, most of us will have a local Sainsbury, and the good news is that the Sainsbury's Special Selection range includes every product you will need on the Japanese Diet.

But there's always a downside, isn't there? In this case it is the fact that only about seventy Sainsbury stores carry the Special Selection range. However, that range is excellent. You will find sake; miso; dashi stock; several kinds of dried seaweed; Japanese wasabi horseradish; even mirin (the sweet rice wine which is harder to find than sake).

So if your local branch isn't one of the Special Selection ones, it is worth while getting in touch with the branch manager and ordering what you need. Here are some of the products that should be on your Sainsbury Japanese shopping list:

Miso paste; **Mitsukan Japanese saifun**; **yaki suishi nori**; **sukiyaki** sauce; **wakame**; **wasabi paste**; **hon-mirin**; **Mitsukan** powdered **sushi** seasoning mix.

For further information about Sainsbury, phone the head office in London on: 0171 921 6000.

ORIENTAL STORES

When my mother and I first started cooking Oriental foods in Liverpool twenty-odd years ago, it really was quite an unusual thing to do, and certainly the trip down to Chinatown to buy the ingredients was a real adventure. These days it is no longer considered eccentric to cook Oriental foods at home and most everyday supermarkets stock all the relevant ingredients. Oriental stores are also much more used to dealing with Gai-Jin (foreigners) or "round-eyes", and at Liverpool Oriental supermarkets you are more likely to have trouble understanding your Chinese assistant's scouse than anything else. Even so, I have never lost that personal sense of adventure and travel when stepping into an Oriental food store. So although you don't really need to visit one before starting the Japanese Diet, I really do think it is worth shopping in a proper Oriental store — if only for the fun of it. There are good Oriental food stores is every major town or city in Britain — if I haven't listed one close enough to you here, then just check your Yellow Pages (under supermarkets or grocers) and you'll be bound to find one.

Specialist Japanese and General Oriental Food Stores

Inner London

Various stores in Gerrard Street, London WI and Lisle Street, London WI.

JA Centre, 348/356 Regent's Park Road, Finchley Central, London N3. Tel: 0181 346 1042.

Japanese Food Centre, 66–68 Brewer Street, London WI. Tel: 0171 439 8035.

Ya'ohan, 339 Edgware Road, London NW9. Tel: 0181 200 0009.

Outer London and South East

Iseya, 182 Preston Road, Wembley, Middlesex. Tel: 0181 908 4530.

Harro, 23a Lombard Road, London SW19. Tel: 0181 543 3343.

South-East

Ayame Japanese Food Store, Unit L13, Gyosei College, Acacia Road, Reading, Berks. Tel: 01734 310670.

Miura Foods, 44 Coombe Road, Kingston, Surrey. Tel: 0181 549 8076.

East

Winfield Supermarket, 58 Mill Road, Cambridge. Tel: 01223 322888.

The Oriental Stores, 37 Newnham Road, Cambridge. Tel: 01223 323178.

South

Wing Wah Chinese Food Market, 119 Clifton Road, Worthing, Sussex. Tel: 01903 211611.

Yau Brothers Oriental, Princes Street, Northam, Southampton, Hants. Tel: 01703 225568/636474.

South-West
Kin Yip Hon Supermarket, 16a St Thomas Street, Bristol. Tel: 0117 929 9098.

Wai Yee Chinese Supermarket, 4 Station Road, Montpelier, Bristol. Tel: 0117 942 8629/8509.

Wing Hing Japanese and Oriental Food Supermarket, 28–34 Lower Ashley Road, St Agnes, Bristol. Tel: 0117 907 1191.

Midlands
Chinese Supermarket, Unit B101, Arcadian Centre, Pershore Street, Birmingham. Tel: 0121 622 6182.

East West Provisions, 61a Woodstock Road, Oxford. Tel: 01865 311288.

Four Seasons, 1 Mill Lane, Enderby, Leicester. Tel: 0116 286 5290.

Janson Hong Ltd, St Martins House, 17–18 Bull Ring, Birmingham. Tel: 0121 643 4681.

Tai Fat Foodstore, 5 Melton Street, Leicester. Tel: 0116 262 9656/5701.

Win Yip, 375 Nechells Park Road, Saltley, Birmingham. Tel: 0121 327 3838.

North-East
Brighton Oriental Food Store, 14–18 Brighton Grove, Newcastle upon Tyne, Tyneside. Tel: 0191 273 1070.

Kung Heng, 169 London Road, Sheffield. Tel: 0114 258 6652.

Maumoniat International Food Supermarket, 39 Brudenell Grove, Leeds. Tel: 0113 275 1887.

Tai Sun Supermarket, 49 College Road, Doncaster. Tel: 01302 344360.

Wing Lee Hong, Hereford House, Edward Street, Leeds. Tel: 0113 245 7203.

North-West
Shun On Chinese Supermarket, 27 Berry Street, Liverpool. Tel: 0151 708 0844.

Yu Hing Supermarket, 45a Faulkner Street, Manchester. Tel: 0161
236 4152/9288.

Wales

Eastern Chinese Supermarket, 26 Tudor Street, Riverside, Cardiff.
Tel: 01222 397148/388906.
Far East Groceries, 15 Abergele Road, Colwyn Bay, Clwyd. Tel:
01492 532251.
The China Supermarket, 32–34 Tudor Street, Cardiff. Tel: 01222
377599.

Scotland

Chinatown Groceries, Unit 9–10, Chinatown Shopping Mall, 42
New City Road, Glasgow. Tel: 0141 332 9399.
Oriental supermarkets in Leith Walk, Edinburgh.

Japanese Tableware and Household Goods

Inner London

Liberty, 210–220 Regent Street, London W1R 6AH. Tel: 0171 734
1234. Beautiful Arts and Crafts movement period department store
which specialises in unusual homewares; extensive Oriental section.
Well worth a visit.
Muji, 26 Great Marlborough Street, London W1V 1HB. Tel: 0171
494 1197 and 39 Shelton Street, London WC2 1HB. Tel: 0171 379
1331. Now extremely trendy Japanese clothes and homeware store
specialising in very minimalist designs. Definitely something out of
the ordinary.
Neal Street East, 5 Neal Street, London WC2 1HB. Tel: 0171 240
0135. Covent Garden store which was one of the very first to
import Japanese goods into London. Range increasing all the time.
Very good value.
Take Ltd, 45–46 Chalk Farm Road, London NW1 8AJ. Tel: 0171
267 4497. Part of the North London Japanese outpost which started
with the JA Stores chain. Wide range of goods.

Outer London

Take Ltd, 18 Upper Richmond Road, London SW14 8AW. Tel: 0181 876 9216. Further branch of the North London Take group.
Noritake Shop, 19 Heath Field, Milton Keynes. Tel: 01908 318446.

5

WHAT TO BUY

Once you are familiar with it, Japanese food is very simple to prepare and cook, with a whole variety of lovely tastes. However, Japanese cookery uses some unusual ingredients, and even the ones we know well are sometimes prepared differently. Just as a Japanese housewife would be at a loss to know what to do when presented with the traditional British spud fresh from the ground, so we can feel very confused about how to use and prepare many Japanese foods.

This section gives you an overall introduction to the common ingredients, describing what each is, and which are better known in Britain by other names. If it all seems rather confusing, hang on in there. Once you have read the book and the recipes, you will find yourself cooking Japanese foods as easily as you do meat and two veg.

A Guide to the Important Foods

Here is a brief guide to the most important staple foods in Japanese cooking. It tells you all about each one individually and why it is so healthy.

RICE
Just as bread or potatoes are regarded as the basic bulk foods in the Northern European diet, rice is the main bulk carbohydrate food for

the Japanese. It is served with all main meals, cooked in a variety of different ways.

In addition to being delicious, easy to cook, filling and low in calories, rice is also exceptionally rich in healthy nutrients. It is high in fibre, low in cholesterol, a source of B vitamins and the trace element potassium. For those trying to cut down on meat for health and slimming reasons it is pleasant to discover that rice is also a source of protein. It is known as a "second class" protein, which means you have to eat rather more of it than you would of meat to get the same amount of protein. But it still makes a useful contribution to your protein needs without the cholesterol risks of meat. And many people who cannot eat wheat products because of allergy find they can easily switch to rice-based products.

If rice sounds rather a miracle food, you won't be surprised to read that so important is rice in Japan that it has a god of its own, called Inari, and historically rice was used as a unit of taxation and a measure of a man's wealth. Even today the preparation of rice is so highly valued that a cook's skill is measured by the quality of his or her rice dishes – rather like the lightness of pastry is regarded in England.

Ingredient   Rice
Health Benefit   Anti-allergenic; reduces digestive illness

Nutritional information	Cholesterol	Fibre	Saturated fat	Vitamins	Nutritional group	Trace elements
	low	high	low	B group	carbohydrate and protein	potassium

SOYA

After rice, the soya bean is probably the most important element of the Japanese Diet, and according to new research into heart disease, from the health point of view it may be the most important of all. A very recent study aimed at finding out why there is so little heart disease in Japan has identified the high levels of soya bean and soya products eaten as producing a protective effect against the cardio-vascular problems which lead to heart disease and heart attacks. The study found benefits from as little as 25g/1oz of soya protein a day, although 50g/2oz was better.

Soya beans contain a number of plant compounds called phytoestrogens which may have medicinal qualities. They also occur in smaller quantities in rye, wheat, corn, carrots, sesame and sunflower seeds. The phytoestrogens behave like natural oestrogen made by the body, reducing the risk of cancer, improving menopausal symptoms and reducing LDL (bad) cholesterol. The effectiveness of soya has also been confirmed by the much lower rates of heart disease and cancer in many Asian countries where it is a staple food. Soya's powers as a "wonder bean" have been proven in other areas including breast cancer, prostate cancer and osteoporosis.

Soya is also rich in magnesium, a vital trace element to balance the body's fluid levels. According to the Women's Nutritional Advisory Foundation, good levels of magnesium help to stop PMT (pre-menstrual tension).

In its use in Japanese cooking the soya bean comes in four different forms:

○ **Whole bean** Whole soya beans are just the Japanese version of the good old British baked bean – indeed, some varieties of canned baked beans use soya as their base bean. You can also buy whole soya beans canned or dried in supermarkets or in health stores and you can use them just as you would any other variety of bean.

○ **Soya bean curd** (tofu) This is a firm, white cheese-like substance with roughly the texture of a soft cheese. It is a very important part of the diet throughout Asia, and though bland when served on its own (a little like plain yoghurt), it is marvellous when cooked as it absorbs the most delicate and subtle flavours. It cooks very quickly and can be used in soups, fry-ups, stews, salads, grills and as a substitute for meat.

○ **Soy sauce** This is perhaps the most familiar use of soya for most

Westerners, since we've all had it on our Chinese take-away.
The Japanese version of soy sauce is milder, less salty and rather
sweeter than the Chinese. Many believe it has a more delicate
flavour but it is really just a matter of personal taste. Unless
specified, either can be used in recipes.

○ **Miso paste** This is a use of soya specific to the Japanese where
the cooked bean is ground up into a powder or paste which
is then used as a stock mix (as we would use a stock cube), a
seasoning or a soup base. Miso soup is the Japanese equivalent
of a clear chicken or beef consommé here.

As vegetarians will know, soya is also an excellent source of
"second-class" non-animal protein. Indeed, soya is the base for
most of the substitute meat products like vegeburgers which are
so popular now. If you don't want to face experimenting directly
with the soya bean curd which is used in some of the recipes, you
could try substituting a ready-made soya-based meat substitute.

Ingredient	Soya
Health Benefit	Appears to reduce heart disease; helps PMT; fights breast cancer and osteoporosis and cancer of the prostate

Nutritional information	Cholesterol	Fibre	Saturated fat	Vitamins	Nutritional group	Trace elements
	low	high in whole beans	low	B group	carbohydrate and protein	potassium, calcium, magnesium, zinc, iron

FISH AND SEAFOOD

This is the major source of protein in the Japanese Diet. The Japanese
eat more fish per head of the population than any other people in
the world, nearly half a kilo (a pound) every week.

Fish oils are rich sources of essential fatty acids (EFAs). You have
probably seen these mentioned before, since scientists now believe

that the role of EFAs is very important in the battle against heart disease. In fact many nutritional supplements are now on the market which contain these EFAs. Some have quite high levels of vitamins A and D, which can be dangerous in excess (particularly for pregnant women), so it is probably best to do as the Japanese do and get your EFA direct from the fish, since fish are relatively low in all vitamins including A and D.

How do EFAs work against heart disease? Basically what they do is thin the blood by encouraging the formation of hormones called prostaglandins. In turn the prostaglandins are believed to work against the formation of blood clots in the circulatory system. These prostaglandin group hormones also help reduce levels of fat circulating in the blood and increase the amount of HDL cholesterol (the "good" cholesterol, LDL is the bad one). All this contributes to reduce the risk of heart disease and stroke.

The Japanese are particularly good at different ways of cooking fish. An old text describes a hundred ways of cooking sea bream (called "tai" in Japanese) which is very much a luxury food. There may not be so many in this book, but you will certainly enjoy learning lots of new, cheap and simple ways of incorporating more fish into your diet.

Many of us are already including more seafood in our diet, especially prawns and shrimps. Supermarkets are stocking fresh green-lipped mussels on their fish counters, which is great news for those with arthritis. There are lots of recipes in the book to help you use the possibilities of seafood to the maximum.

Ingredient	Fish and Seafood
Health Benefit	Reduces risk of heart disease and stroke; green-lipped mussels help arthritis

Nutritional information	Cholesterol	Fibre	Saturated fat	Vitamins	Nutritional group	Trace elements
	increases HDL in blood	low	low	E	protein	Essential Fatty Acids

SEA VEGETABLES

Seaweed is an important vegetable for the Japanese, and don't forget that it has also been eaten historically in Britain where laver ("nori" in Japanese) is a Welsh delicacy, and the beach shrub samphire is a luxury vegetable from the East Coast.

The two main sea vegetables eaten in Japan are nori (laver) and kombu (translates to kelp in English). Other Japanese seaweeds include wakame and arame, which are not eaten as often.

They are eaten not only for their flavour but also for their health-giving properties. They are especially rich in iodine which acts on the thyroid to increase metabolic activity and can therefore aid slimming – especially for those whose underactive thyroid gland has made it difficult for them to lose weight in the past.

According to Dr Leonard Mervyn, author of *Vitamins and Minerals*: "Deficiency of iodine is an important world health problem. At least 200 million people suffer from diseases traced to lack of the mineral."

Most of us gain the iodine we need as a trace element which leaches into our food and water from the soil, so in areas where there is little iodine in the soil, deficiency can become a problem. Severe deficiency causes a swelling disease of the thyroid gland called goitre, but even mild deficiency can give rise to a variety of problems. The thyroid controls our metabolism, the way we convert food into energy and how we use that energy. When the thyroid becomes underactive due to deficiency of iodine, the whole metabolism slows down causing weight gain, lethargy, tiredness and muscle weakness. Replenishing the deficiency sparks the thyroid back into life and can make a huge difference for sufferers.

The distribution of iodine world-wide is very erratic, so deficiency problems are widespread. In the US it is a familiar characteristic of sleepy, slow-paced Middle America, and in Britain goitre is often known as Derbyshire Neck because the condition is so well known there.

Taken in excess, though, iodine can be poisonous, so buying a manufactured iodine supplement is not always a good idea. It is much better to let the Japanese Diet stabilise your iodine levels the natural way by adding small amounts of sea vegetables to your eating. Please don't be put-off by this. The Japanese have developed excellent convenience-food ways of packaging seaweed so that it is quite unrecognisable from the stuff on the beach, and the taste is delicious. If you still hate the idea, spring greens can be substituted in many cases — but don't forget, you'll be missing out on all that metabolism-boosting iodine.

Ingredient   Seaweed/Sea Vegetables
Health Benefit Stimulate thyroid to raise metabolism and reduce obesity

Nutritional information	Cholesterol	Fibre	Saturated fat	Vitamins	Nutritional group	Trace elements
	low	medium	low	medium levels	vegetable	iodine, potassium, calcium, magnesium, iron

FRESH VEGETABLES AND MUSHROOMS

From the health expert's point of view one of the key factors in the Japanese Diet is the amount of fresh, raw, or lightly cooked vegetables it provides. These are rich in the key vitamins A, C and E which are now thought to play such an important role in many body functions.

These vitamins are anti-oxidants. That is, they help offset the effects of the degenerative process of oxidation that goes on in the body all the time and is an inevitable result of simply living and breathing. Oxidation occurs when a material reacts with oxygen and decays as a result. The most obvious example of oxidation in day-to-day life is when something rusts. Of course our bodies are not rusting up inside! But basically the same process is going on, with equally destructive side effects.

The anti-oxidant vitamins can slow down this process and prevent the side effects from being too disruptive. A good supply of these vitamins also boosts the immune system.

But perhaps most important is the role that scientists believe they play in cancer prevention, and even cure. Professor Karol Sikora, a leading cancer researcher, says that apart from not smoking, getting plenty of A, C and E vitamins is your best bet in the fight against cancer.

One vegetable which is especially popular with the Japanese doesn't have the A, C and E group in it – but it is rich in the other main group, the B vitamins. The Japanese shiitake mushroom (on sale in Waitrose and other supermarkets) is especially interesting because some recent studies pointed to its having a role in reducing cholesterol levels. So because the Japanese Diet includes all these foods, you will be getting a wonderful all-round vitamin boost.

A particular virtue of the shiitake mushroom is that it is so easy to cultivate, even given very limited resources, and it is seen as being a potential super-crop for Third World development. The pioneer in this field is the Japanese company Kanebo – which most of us in Britain associate with cosmetics. But in Japan there is often a huge amount of cross-over in the fields of health, nutrition and beauty, as you will discover throughout this book.

Another important vegetable for the Japanese is the humble radish, which gives Japanese cookery much of its distinctive flavour and piquancy. The variety of radish most often used is the "daikon" – a large white radish which is much milder than the familiar fiery red ones. Many supermarkets and specialist stores stock the daikon radish, but if you can't find it, horseradish or horseradish sauce can often be used in recipes as a substitute.

| **Ingredient** | Fresh Vegetables/Mushrooms |
| **Health Benefit** | Anti-oxidant; immune system booster; cancer preventative; anti-cholesterol |

Nutritional information	**Cholesterol**	**Fibre**	**Saturated fat**	**Vitamins**	**Nutritional group**	**Trace elements**
	low	high	low	A, B, C, E	vegetable	many

A – Z of Ingredients

The Japanese Diet includes some specialist foods and ingredients which you may not already have in your larder. Some readers will be aware of these ingredients from eating out and they are available in national supermarket chains (see pages 42–5). This section describes these ingredients and lists the major suppliers. Where you may want to substitute a different ingredient, alternatives are given. But generally you will find that most of the main items are ones you use occasionally in any case. Japan borrows extensively from Chinese cooking so this makes it even easier to find a wide range of familiar, enjoyable and easily obtained foods and ingredients.

BAMBOO SHOOTS
The Japanese use fresh bamboo shoots when they are in season, and sometimes these are available here in specialist groceries and Oriental supermarkets. Most of the time, however, you will be using canned bamboo shoots which should be drained before cooking.

Availability:
- Tesco – Amoy sliced bamboo shoots; Lotus sliced bamboo shoots.
- Waitrose – canned Amoy bamboo shoots (canned vegetables section).
- Safeway – own-brand sliced bamboo shoots in water (canned goods section).
- Also: Oriental stores, delicatessens; fresh from specialist grocers occasionally.

Substitute: not recommended, but slivered carrots or celery can be used.

BEAN CURD
Also sold under the name tofu, comes ready-packed or loose, fresh or smoked. Sold in its own liquid which needs to be drained before cooking.

Availability:
- ○ Tesco – Sanchi tofu; Cauldron Foods marinated tofu pieces; Cauldron Foods original tofu.
- ○ Waitrose – Sanchi tofu pre-packed; Cauldron original tofu; Cauldron marinated tofu.
- ○ Safeway – Cauldron Foods original tofu; Cauldron Foods marinated tofu pieces (in chilled vegetarian section).
- ○ Also: health food shops and Oriental stores; loose in Oriental stores and some health food shops and delicatessens.

CHILLI SAUCE

A very wide range of chilli sauces is available in the bottled sauce section of your supermarket's shelves, and you will often find even more when you look at the ethnic food sections now being set up in most chains. Brands like Sharwood's and Amoy provide some excellent chilli sauces. Try and find one with a sweet overtone – often labelled Thai, Singapore or Japanese chilli sauce. Look where the other ketchups and sauces are stocked in supermarkets, delicatessens and Oriental stores.

Availability:
- ○ Tesco – Natco crushed chillies.
- ○ Waitrose – own-brand hot chilli; Amoy chilli sauce; Sharwood's chilli sauce; Blue Dragon chilli sauce.

Substitute: no need to substitute, but you may want to experiment to find a chilli sauce you really like.

DASHI STOCK

Dashi stock is made from kombu ("kelp") and dried fish flakes ("bonito"). It is sold as an instant powder in Japanese and Oriental stores and is also available from traditional supermarket chains. It is very much the Japanese equivalent of a stock cube, although its flavour is rather more unusual. If you cannot find the instant powder, a recipe is given for making your own (see page 78), or you can use a substitute.

Availability:
- ○ Tesco – Lotus Chinese vegetable soup; Lotus Chinese hot and sour soup, Sharwood's classic Chinese marinade; Sanchi miso soup, Sanchi mugi miso.
- ○ Waitrose – Blue Dragon fish sauce.
- ○ Sainsbury – dashi no moto soup stock in the Special Selection range.
- ○ Also: Japanese and Oriental specialist stores.

Substitute: close substitutes are tinned consommé, stock cubes and soup mixes.

FISH AND SEAFOOD

Buy fresh fish on the day you cook it. If using frozen, defrost carefully. Fortunately supermarket counters and fishmongers are now much more imaginatively stocked. Don't be shy about asking the fish counter to prepare your fish for you and for any tips on cooking – the major supermarket chains are especially good about this. Oriental supermarkets often stock unusual varieties of fresh or frozen fish – but frankly, I don't recommend buying them!

Availability: supermarkets, fishmongers.
Substitute: none.

DRIED FRUITS

To be truly authentic we would be using umeboshi which is a kind of pickled sweet/sour plum much used in Japanese cooking and considered to have medicinal properties (see page 70). However, this is both difficult to obtain and can be something of an acquired taste. Alternatives are bottled, crystallised and spiced fruits as well as dried fruits, but these can be luxury items in Britain, so I have referred mainly to dried fruits in the recipes. If you can get hold of umeboshi and want to give them a try, then do experiment where the recipe mentions dried spiced fruit.

Availability: supermarkets, grocers, delicatessens.
Substitute: none needed.

FRESH HERBS

The main fresh herbs you will need are coriander and parsley. The best place to look for these is in the grocery section of your supermarket. If you get adventurous you can also find some wonderful Chinese and Japanese salads at Oriental stores, and even in the supermarket, so do add them to your repertoire.

Availability:
- ○ Tesco – Schwartz coriander; Schwartz lemon grass.
- ◐ Waitrose – Chinese chives; lemon grass; coriander, etc. (in the fresh vegetables section); Barts dried chilli, coriander, lemon grass, Thai paste (in herbs and spices section).

Substitute: none needed.

GINGER

Ginger is very highly thought of in China and Japan. It is regarded as health-giving, and special porcelain jars are made to keep it in. But in Britain we don't think about ginger very much. It is there if you look for it though, both fresh and preserved.

The recipes in this book use two different forms of ginger. **Fresh root ginger** is a grocery item sold alongside the garlic bulbs. It should be peeled before use. **Crystallised stem ginger** is sweet and is usually stocked along with the jams or on the luxury foods shelf. It only needs to be chopped before use, and the syrup is excellent for adding to marinade mixes.

Availability:
- ○ Tesco – Uncle Ben's sweet and sour ginger (cooking sauce); John West fresh minced ginger.
- ○ Waitrose – Barts dried ginger; fresh root ginger.
- ○ Safeway – Opies crystallised stem ginger (ingredients and decorations section).

Substitute: none.

HOISIN PASTE

This is originally a Chinese ingredient. It is used in marinades and sauces, giving added piquancy. Since the explosion of interest in

Chinese cooking, hoisin sauce (or paste) is now much easier to find, with leading names including Sharwood's producing it. So popular is it now that it is almost mainstream, and you will find it somewhere near the sauces or ethnic section in your supermarket.

Availability:
○ Tesco — Merrychef hoisin sauce.
○ Waitrose — Sharwood's hoisin sauce.
○ Also: Oriental stores, delicatessens.
Substitute: a fairly unusual taste not easily substituted.

MISO PASTE

This is about the only uniquely Japanese ingredient included in this diet. I have only mentioned it in a couple of recipes, and substitutes are suggested. The reason for this is that not only is it quite difficult to get hold of, but it is also something of an acquired taste. Miso is basically a thick paste made out of ground soya bean and it is mainly used in soups.

Availability:

○ Tesco — Sanchi miso soup, Sanchi mugi miso.
○ Sainsbury — miso soya bean paste (hanamaruki) from the Special Selection range.
○ Also: Japanese specialist stores.
Substitute: stock cube.

MUSHROOMS

Mushrooms play an important part in Japanese cuisine, but not just any mushrooms. There is a whole range of fresh and dried Japanese mushrooms which taste delicious, and may well have health benefits too. Shiitake mushrooms are sold fresh in supermarkets and at some groceries.

Dried Japanese mushrooms are sold in Oriental supermarkets and some delicatessens. They should be soaked thoroughly before use and the water discarded. The quickest way to get them to take in the water is to pour on boiling water and let them sit in it as it cools for a couple of hours.

Availability:
- ○ Waitrose – fresh shiitake mushrooms (in fresh vegetables section); dried shiitake mushrooms.
- ○ Also: Oriental stores, grocers, delicatessens.

Substitute: English mushrooms.

NOODLES

There are a huge number of different types of noodles used in Oriental cooking. The easiest to use are the special packs which you can get in supermarkets as well as Oriental stores. These contain dried noodles (they look curly, rather like crimped hair) plus little packs of stock powder to make up into stock in which the noodles are cooked. Another variety which is slightly more difficult to prepare but very spectacular when cooked is the transparent, cellophane noodle. Again these are dried and come in wrapped bundles. It is a good idea to soak the noodles briefly before cooking with them.

Availability:
- ○ Tesco – Vesta chow mein crispy noodles; Top ramen Japanese noodles (various flavours); Doll instant noodles (various flavours); Sharwood's noodles; Sharwood's thread noodles; Blue Dragon crispy noodles.
- ○ Waitrose – Conimex rice noodles; a variety of Chinese noodles.
- ○ Sainsbury – Soba Japanese buckwheat noodles (shimadaya) from the Special Selection range.
- ○ Also: Oriental stores, delicatessens.

Substitute: spaghetti.

NORI AND KOMBU SEAWEED

Nori comes pre-packed and looks all shiny and green. It is prepared in thin dry sheets or strips and used as a wrapping, garnish or snack. As a snack you should heat it until it is dry and brittle and then dip in soy sauce.

Kombu (kelp) is dried in thick sheets and used in soups and stocks. You will come across it in health food stores and some delicatessens as well as Oriental supermarkets. Other less often used seaweeds include arame and wakame.

Availability:
○ Tesco – Sanchi kombu; Sanchi arame seaweed; Sanchi Wakame seaweed; Sanchi nori seaweed.
○ Waitrose – own-brand seaweed (in prepared meal section); wakame fresh seaweed.
○ Sainsbury – yaki sushi nori (dried nori seaweed); fueru wakame; wel pac (dried kelp seaweed).
○ Also: health food stores, Oriental stores, some fishmongers.
Substitute: whole leaves of fresh spring greens.

NUTS
These may be in your store cupboard already, but if not, get in a couple of packs of walnuts, almonds or hazelnuts.

Availability: supermarkets, grocers, delicatessens.
Substitute: none.

PICKLED CABBAGE
You can get authentic Japanese and Chinese pickled vegetables from Oriental stores. The Japanese especially make a large range of pickles, but if you are going to buy just one, cabbage is probably the best. A jar of pickled cabbage keeps very well in the store cupboard, so buy one when you begin the diet and you can dip into it for many different recipes.

Availability:
○ Tesco – Suzi-Wan Chinese salad (pickles section); Suzi-Wan Thai salad (pickles section).
○ Also: Oriental stores, some delicatessens.
Substitute: winter cabbage shredded fine with a vinegar dressing.

PLUM SAUCE
Another of those more or less unique sweet/sour Oriental tastes. This is very useful for marinades, dipping sauces and jazzing up rice

dishes. So it is well worth investing in a jar. It keeps well in a cool store cupboard or the fridge.

Availability:
O Tesco – Merrychef plum sauce.
O Waitrose – Sharwood's plum sauce.
O Also: Oriental stores.
Substitute: mix honey or jam with some soy sauce.

RADISH AND HORSERADISH

The radish variety the Japanese prefer is a large white one called a daikon, much milder than the hot red radishes. Quite a few supermarkets and grocers stock these and they provide such a good flavour to dishes that it is well worth looking out for them.

A jar of horseradish sauce would be a good buy for the store cupboard as it gives a remarkably authentic flavour to dishes – especially if you can't get hold of daikon. The Japanese version of horseradish is called wasabi, a hot, green spice. Originally the root of the wasabi plant was grated for use as a spice in sushi or as a condiment with noodles, but nowadays it is available ready-packed in powdered or chipped form.

Availability:
O Tesco – Sanchi hot and spicy wasabi chips.
O Sainsbury – wasabi paste (prepared Japanese horseradish) in the Special Selection range
O Also: greengrocers.
Substitute: horseradish sauce.

RICE

Fortunately most supermarkets have a huge range of different varieties of rice, so getting the right ones for this diet is not a problem. You will need plenty of short grain (also called round or risotto) rice, and it is a good idea to get in some long grain and maybe even some wild rice as well to add variety, since a great deal of rice is eaten on the Japanese Diet.

Availability:
○ Tesco – own-brand risotto (round grain) rice; Tilda Thai jasmine rice; Sea Isle long grain pre-fluffed rice (great for crispy rice dishes).
○ Sainsbury – Japanese rice in the Special Selection range.
○ Also: most supermarkets have an own-brand round or risotto rice.
Substitute: not necessary.

RICE CAKES
Many Western food manufacturers now make rice cakes and you will find them in the crispbread section of the supermarket. Rice cakes are excellent for those wanting to slim on the Japanese Diet. They are very nourishing and filling, at the same time as being low in calories and fat. This makes them an invaluable nibble food for times when slimming fatigue strikes.

Availability:
○ Tesco – Healthy Choice Rice Cakes.
○ Safeway – Lyons **SliceaRice**; Kallo Rice Cakes (crispbreads section).
Substitute: not necessary.

SAKE
The universal Japanese alcoholic beverage, made from rice, usually served warm with meals as well as being used extensively in cooking. This diet does not include it as a beverage, but it is in many of the recipes so it is a good idea to get a bottle in, much as you would have a bottle of cooking sherry.

Mirin is a sweetened version of sake used in marinades and for sweet seasoning. If you can get it from an Oriental store it is very useful, otherwise you can substitute sweet sherry.

Availability: off-licences; some supermarket off-licence sections; Oriental store off-licence sections.
Substitute: cooking sherry.

SESAME OIL
A very high-quality cooking oil made from ground sesame seeds. It has a distinctive smoky flavour which permeates food cooked in it. One large bottle will last a long time as it is a very good coating oil. It is also extremely healthy, being low in saturated fat and high in polyunsaturates. So many supermarkets now stock such wide ranges of different cooking oils that you are very likely to come across it alongside olive oil.

Availability:
O Tesco – Tesco sesame oil; Lotus sesame oil; Amoy sesame oil.
O Waitrose – own-brand sesame oil.
O Safeway – own-brand toasted sesame oil.
Substitute: olive oil with added sesame seeds.

SESAME SEEDS
Whole sesame seeds are used in many dishes for flavour, texture and appearance. Expect to find them either somewhere near the herb and spice section or with the other Oriental food ranges.

Availability:
O Tesco – own-brand sesame seeds; Hunni Foods sesame seeds.
O Waitrose – own-brand (in fresh vegetables section).
Substitute: hard to substitute.

SOYA BEANS
The whole beans are usually sold dried by the packet along with the other beans and pulses in the dried food section of the supermarket. Some shops also stock ready-cooked, canned soya beans. Either is equally good, although the canned beans are more convenient.

Availability: supermarkets, Oriental stores, delicatessens.
Substitute: mung beans, black eyed beans.

SOYA OIL
A very popular and inexpensive oil which you will find alongside corn oil in the supermarket. Many of the leading brands of

polyunsaturated cooking oil in fact use soya as the base oil – so you may find you have already been cooking with soya oil for some time.

Availability:
◐ Tesco – Soya pure soya oil; Tesco stir-fry oil.
Substitute: sunflower oil.

SOY SAUCE

Now a very familiar condiment in Britain which you can expect to see alongside Worcester sauce and Branston pickle on the supermarket shelves. You may also find it in the ethnic speciality section. There are several different kinds of soy sauce. The normal dark one which most people use is actually quite salty. For Japanese cooking it is better to use the light version, which will be labelled "light soy sauce" and which is actually lighter in colour than the normal rich version. If you are making the trip to a specialist Oriental store, then buy Japanese soy sauce, but if you don't have the opportunity, light soy sauce will be equally good.

Availability:
○ Tesco – Sharwood's light soy sauce; Kikkoman soy sauce; Lotus light soy sauce; Lea & Perrins soy and five spice sauce; Amoy light soy sauce.
○ Waitrose – Sharwood's light soy sauce; Kikkoman Japanese soy sauce; Amoy light soy sauce.
○ Sainsbury – Yamasa Japanese soy sauce in the Special Selection range.
○ Also: Oriental stores, delicatessens.
Substitute: not necessary.

SPICES

Very much a key note of Chinese cooking, five spice powder is also used in several Japanese recipes. Ready-mixed five spice powder in now available in Western shops as well as Oriental specialists;

just check the herbs and spices section of your supermarket. For a sweeter, more Westernised version of the powder, try the mixed spice option available in most ranges. You will also need some paprika.

Availability:
- ○ Tesco – Schwartz rice seasoning; Sharwood's five spice powder; Suzi-Wan five spice sauce.
- ○ Waitrose – Conimex nasi goreng; Lea & Perrins five spice soy sauce.
- ○ Also: Oriental stores.

Substitute: mixed spice.

SUNFLOWER SEEDS

Now a popular nibble food, salad topping and snack, packets of sunflower seeds can usually be found in one of two places in the supermarket – either masquerading as a salad component in the grocery section, or with the potato crisps. If you have no luck in the supermarket, your local health food store will certainly have some, since they are rich in polyunsaturated oil and a great favourite with vegetarians.

Availability:
- ○ Tesco – own-brand sunflower seeds.
- ○ Waitrose – fresh sunflower seeds in fresh vegetables section.
- ○ Also: health food stores.

Substitute: nuts; pine kernels.

TERIYAKI SAUCE

Like soy sauce, which it closely resembles, this Japanese condiment is now generally popular. It is slightly harder to get hold of than soy sauce, but many of the leading Oriental brands like Sharwood's and Amoy now make it, so if you look for it in the speciality foods section of the supermarket you will probably find it. Otherwise Oriental stores stock it, as do some health food stores and delicatessens.

Availability:
- ○ Tesco – Amoy teriyaki sauce; Lawrys teriyaki barbecue sauce; Sharwood's stir-fry teriyaki.
- ○ Waitrose – Kikkoman teriyaki sauce; Sharwood's stir-fry teriyaki.
- ○ Sainsbury – also have a sukiyaki sauce.

Substitute: soy sauce sweetened with brown sugar.

UMEBOSHI PLUMS

Umeboshi plums can be pickled at home in brine, though nowadays they are more commonly bought already pickled. They are often used as a relish inside rice balls or in a lunch box. The red of the plum on a background of white rice is favoured for its resemblance to the Japanese flag. They are believed to promote digestion. Umeboshi plums are generally only available in Japanese stores, so none of the recipes given in this book use them, but if you find some and want to use them, do so where the recipe calls for dried fruit.

Availability: specialist Oriental stores.
Substitute: dried fruit.

VINEGAR

Vinegar is an important ingredient in the light sauce which Japanese very often serve with rice. It is also used extensively in marinades, so it is a good idea to have some in the store cupboard. Unfortunately, in order to produce authentic Japanese flavours you will need to use both wine vinegar and malt vinegar – but both last for ever in the cupboard.

Availability:
- ○ Tesco – Carbonell sherry vinegar, especially recommended.
- ○ Sainsbury – Marukan rice vinegar in the Special Selection range.
- ○ Also: most supermarkets, health food stores.
  Substitute: not necessary.

PART TWO

6

JAPANESE PREPARATION AND COOKING METHODS

Part of the fun of being on the Japanese Diet is experimenting with all the new cooking techniques that are used in Oriental cuisine. The last thing you will find yourself doing is complaining about yet another boring old salad or baked potato, as one tends to do on ordinary diets.

There is such a variety of methods of cooking, that even the same ingredients can taste completely different cooked in different ways. And because so much Japanese food is cooked at the table, by the diners themselves, you will find your family and friends become enthusiastic to join in – another advantage over the standard two-celery-sticks diet.

However, some of the Japanese cooking and presentation methods are only just beginning to become well known in the West, so this section gives you a brief introduction to them.

Like Chinese cuisine, Japanese cooking is governed by five major flavours – hot, sweet, sour, bitter and salty – which are related to the various stocks, sauces and seasonings used such as miso, mirin (sweet rice wine), vinegar, soy sauce and salt. Chilli, radish and ginger provide hotness; sweet rice wine, sugar and plum sauce provide sweet; sour comes from vinegar; dashi fish stock and miso paste have the bitter taste; and salt comes from soy sauce.

Soups accompany every meal in Japan, with the most common

type being miso soup, made from soya bean paste. There is detailed information on miso soup in the recipes section, but since it is an acquired taste it is completely optional on this diet. Japanese food adapts well to Western-style eating, so it is not necessary to be completely authentic and have soup with every meal. Nor do you have to use chopsticks and a bowl — an ordinary knife, fork and plate will do.

Preparing Rice

I think every cook has his or her own particular magic method for making good rice, so these suggestions are only really tips to get you going if you are not an adept rice cooker. The first point is to buy the right rice for the job. Long grain or American rice is most commonly used in this country, but in Japan short or round grain rice is more common. For recipes which require the rice to have sticking qualities (eg, sushi snacks), choose short grain. The recipe will always indicate if you need to use short grain rather than long grain.

To cook short grain rice it is recommended that you rinse or soak the rice for some time before cooking it. I don't usually bother with this (the recipes will tell you if it's important to do it), but I do allow a little extra water when cooking. Exactly how much water to use I'm afraid you will have to discover by trial and error. Generally, enough water to cover the rice and a little extra is the formula given. By the time the rice is cooked, all the water will usually have soaked in, so no draining is required. If you get the proportions wrong either just add as much extra water as you need during cooking, or if you have used too much water, drain it off after cooking. The aim is to get your rice as light and fluffy as possible without it becoming sloppy, watery or tasteless. Always check and stir your rice while it is cooking.

To make rice cooking easier, specialist rice steamers can now be bought from cook shops and Oriental stores, and there are also stock cubes made especially for rice which improve its flavour and appearance tremendously.

Preparing Soya Bean Curd (Tofu)

Soya bean curd or tofu comes in all sorts of forms, but the most widely available is pre-packed in its own liquid. Before you use it you will need to drain the liquid. It is quite soft, and if you want to make it firmer you can poach it gently in stock or water. This is useful if you are then going to grill the bean curd. Other forms of bean curd which come ready-poached or smoked are firm in texture and have more of their own flavour. These versions are mainly available from Oriental supermarkets and sometimes health food stores. They are very versatile – you can chop them straight into soups, salads and stews or stir-fry, grill or barbecue them. The recipes given in this book are for the pre-packed version because it is easier to buy and keep, but if you come across the other versions, feel free to experiment. Here is a guide on the many different ways of using and cooking tofu bean curd.

Steaming – Heats the bean curd (tofu) quickly without losing valuable vitamins and is a fat-free, low-calorie method of cooking. Place the bean curd in a heat-proof dish with a lid (a rice pot is ideal, see page 124) and then either steam it in a purpose-made steamer pan or rest the dish on top of a stand or upturned pot in the steamer. Steaming times vary according to recipe, but about 10 minutes is usual.

Scrambling – Turns bean curd (tofu) into a useful ingredient in mixed and pan-fried dishes and can be used in place of beaten egg or cottage cheese. Place bean curd in a greased or non-stick saucepan, sprinkle with salt and start cooking, scrambling up into pieces with a wooden spoon as you cook. At this point you can either incorporate bean curd directly into your recipe or you can remove it from the heat and drain away the watery juice. Put the remaining curd in a cloth and squeeze out any further juice. This leaves you with a firm-textured curd for cooking or salads etc.

Pressing – This is another way of getting a firm curd for use in salads, canapés and cooking. Wrap bean curd (tofu) in folded cotton teatowel and place on a board on the sink drainer. Prop up one end of the board slightly and then place another board on top.

75

Weight this down (you need about 500g–1kg/1–2lb); use cans of baked beans if you have no weights. After about 20 minutes the liquid will have been pressed out, leaving the bean curd firm.

Blending – For dips, salad dressings, sauces etc you can purée the bean curd (tofu) into a smooth creamy paste in your blender. Add the liquid elements of the recipe at the same time so as not to overwork the blender and increase the smoothness of the end product.

Parboiling – This is useful for firming and freshening bean curd (tofu) as well as imparting flavour, if the liquid used is a stock. Place bean curd in boiling water and leave for about 1 minute before carefully lifting out (a slotted spoon or fish slice is useful) and setting aside to cool. **Draining** – This will be the method you probably use most often, especially if you are mainly using bean curd (tofu) in soups, stews and stir-fry. Put the bean curd in a colander over a bowl and leave in the fridge for about 1 hour for all the liquid to drain off.

Preparing Vegetables and Dried Mushrooms

The key to the health qualities of Japanese cuisine is to avoid overcooking and this is especially true of vegetables, which can easily lose their vitamin content if cooked for too long. Nor should you try to keep vegetables for a long time because this also reduces vitamin content.

Cutting and chopping vegetables into small pieces before cooking means that they do not have to be cooked for so long in order to tenderise. Chop carrots for example into match sticks for quick stir-frying. When boiling, use the blanching technique of plunging the vegetables into water that is already on a high boil, and not leaving the vegetables in for more than a couple of minutes.

Dried mushrooms will need to be soaked to rehydrate them before you use them. There are several ways of doing this. If you know you are going to use dried mushrooms in a recipe the following day, just put them in a large bowl of water overnight.

When you are ready to cook, drain off the liquid and use the mushrooms as instructed. A quick way of rehydrating mushrooms is to put them in a bowl and then pour a kettleful of boiling water over them. They will rehydrate and soften quite quickly and by the time the water has cooled to lukewarm you will be able to drain and use them. Use your common sense about how thoroughly re-hydrated your mushrooms need to be. If you are making a high liquid recipe like a stock, soup or stew then the mushrooms can contine to re-hydrate while cooking, and will absorb the flavours of the cooking liquid. If you are cooking a relatively dry recipe, like a stir-fry, then you need to make sure your mushrooms are completely soft and re-hydrated.

Preparing Fish

Generally make sure that your fish is fresh and thoroughly cleaned. You can substitute frozen fish if you can't get suitable fresh fish, but make sure you defrost it thoroughly and carefully. Never be tempted to cook fish for too long. If you are cooking a whole fish, look at the eye, which goes opaque when the fish is cooked. Otherwise watch for the flesh colouring up and firming.

The Japanese have a great reputation for eating their fish raw, but if you don't feel adventurous about this, there is absolutely no need to try it. You can get just as much nutritional value from your fish cooked as raw, so the Japanese Diet doesn't include raw fish — although if you do get bold later on, there are some recipes for authentic Japanese raw fish "sashimi" (see page 150), which actually turns out to be very similar to smoked salmon only cheaper!

Preparing Nori Seaweed

Japanese housewives don't like the idea of messing around with seaweed any more than we do, so when you buy nori it won't

77

look recognisably like seaweed at all – and it never will do, so don't try to rehydrate it. Nori comes in very thin shiny dark green sheets or strips in sealed packets, in which it keeps for a long time. It is completely dried, so continues to keep well even after you have opened the packet as long as you keep it dry.

The recipes give full directions for how to prepare the nori in each specific case, and overall it is extremely simple, since nori is used either just as it is, straight from the pack, or toasted very briefly on one side first.

There are other forms of seaweed available in Japanese stores. Kombu is a form of dried kelp which is used to make stock. If you use this, then discard the kombu after all the flavour has gone into the stock.

The simple message is not to be worried about using seaweed occasionally. The Japanese have refined it down to a convenience food, and you should treat it just like that.

Preparing Dashi Stock

Just as many dishes in Western cuisine depend on a good quality stock, so do Japanese recipes. In the West you find that the stock is usually meat based – either a clarified chicken stock or jellied stock from a ham bone. In Japan the basis of the stock is fish – usually the dried form of the tuna fish, called in Japanese "bonito". The other main ingredient of dashi stock is kombu, a dried, broad-leaved seaweed.

Most Japanese cooks, like their Western counterparts, rarely go to the bother of making their own stock these days, and instead, just like us, they use dashi stock mixes, cubes and ready-prepared stocks. The various forms of instant dashi are available from Oriental supermarkets and some branches of the main British chains (see Where to Buy section pages 42–49). The most readily available is instant dashi powder (dashi no moto in Japanese). To make it up allow 1/2 a teaspoon of powder to 250ml/8 fl oz of water. Substitutes for Dashi stock are ordinary Western stock, consommé and Japanese packet soup mixes. If you are really keen to make your own home-made Dashi (it's not compulsory), here is a recipe.

Ingredients:
You will need a 2 inch/5cm strip of dried kombu, 1 teaspoon of dried, flaked tuna "bonito" fish (called katsuobushi in Japanese) and 250ml/8 fl oz of water.

Method:
Put the kombu and water in a pan together and bring to the boil, stirring constantly. Once the water is boiling, remove the kombu and discard. Add the dried bonito and bring back to the boil. Simmer over a moderate heat for 2 minutes. Allow to cool. Strain the stock into a jug and discard the bonito. This makes about 250ml/8 fl oz.

Cooking Techniques

STIR-FRY
Stir-frying is such a fundamental for Oriental cuisine that for someone who regularly eats Chinese or Japanese-style food it can be hard to remember that this was not a cooking technique used at all in Britain until quite recently, and is still quite a novelty for many cooks. Yet this is such a quick, simple and healthy way of cooking, it is really worthwhile getting to know about it. For a start, there is no mystery to it. It doesn't need a wok (Chinese frying pan) despite what the kitchen equipment shops may try to persuade you; nor does it need a special hob; nor does it require any special technique. If you've ever sweated an onion in butter before making a soup or sauce, then you can stir-fry. The big health benefits of stir-frying are that it is quick which prevents vital vitamins and trace elements from being destroyed during the cooking process; and that it needs far less oil or fat than conventional frying.

Any good large omelette pan will do, preferably non-stick which reduces still further the amount of oil you need use. Essentially what happens is that you heat a couple of teaspoons of the oil of your choice (different oils give different flavours) and then throw on your ingredients in succession, stirring as they fry. Remember to put on first the ingredients that will take the longest time to cook and add the most delicate ingredients last.

If your stir-fry is too dry or is sticking or you want a sauce, you just add liquid while you're cooking. In Japan the liquid most often added is stock. It is worthwhile having stock ready in the fridge, as a lot of the recipes use stock in them, whether for stir-frying or in a marinade or even in dipping sauces.

Here are a few tips on stir-frying:

○ Use a non-stick frying pan with steep sides (non-stick means you need even less oil, steep sides stop ingredients from going flying).
○ A simple wooden spatula is best for stirring.
○ Get the oil hot before you start adding ingredients (hot oil is more runny and coats quicker, meaning you need less and decreasing risk of burning and sticking).
○ Use a high heat but don't go away from the pan while cooking, keep watching and stirring the whole time.
○ Don't cook for too long – even the toughest ingredients seldom need more than five minutes.
○ Chop or slice longer-cook ingredients like meat and tough vegetables into small pieces to help them cook through quicker.
○ Don't remove one ingredient before cooking another, just keep adding it all into the same pan.
○ Put things that need longest cooking time into the pan first (eg, carrots, other root vegetables, meat) and add the more delicate foods (eg cucumber, lettuce, fish) last.

MARINADE

With Japanese foods traditionally cooked only very lightly, the use of a marinade becomes an important part of many recipes. Cooking the food lightly means the nutritional qualities and flavour are preserved, while using a marinade acts as a partial cooking process in itself – tenderising and killing bacteria prior to cooking. Specific marinade ingredients are given in individual recipes, but here are a few general guidelines:

○ Always include an ingredient with anti-bacterial properties in the marinade – eg, vinegar or alcohol.
○ Make sure the item being marinated is thoroughly steeped in the marinade and that it has a chance to soak in everywhere.
○ Always cover the marinating dish whether you are letting it stand in the fridge or at room temperature.
○ Meat dishes benefit from being marinated at room temperature whereas fish should always be marinated in the fridge.
○ Average marinating times vary from twenty minutes for fish to two hours for meat.

SUSHI

We've all heard of sushi snacks, and some of us have even eaten them in restaurants. They look so pretty, all those bite-size pieces of rice decorated with fish or seafood, or wrapped in seaweed or in strips of the Japanese version of smoked salmon. They remind you of cocktail canapés but are much more unusual. The general verdict is "delicious but I couldn't possibly make them myself".

Some of us are also put off by having heard that the name sushi is Japanese for marinated fish (uncooked). Technically that is true, but it doesn't mean that you have to wrestle with raw fish to enjoy a sushi snack. There are lots of different versions that you can make which preserve the spirit of a sushi snack (called in Japanese "nigiri sushi") without actually involving anything too adventurous.

Nor is it very time-consuming to prepare. In fact, along with sashimi (salted or vinegared raw fish eaten with the rice served separately) the sushi snack is the hamburger of Japan, and it is just as easy to make. In Japan there is a big boom in take-away sushi and there are many new Western ingredients being added (including mayonnaise!)

The origins of sushi can be traced as far back as the Heian Period (794–1185), when the word was used to refer not to any particular

81

dish, but to a method of preserving fish and meat. The "su" of sushi means vinegar, and this is still reflected in the vinegared rice used to prepare sushi dishes.

If you are going to try sushi in a Japanese restaurant, why not impress your friends by ordering them by name! Here is a quick reference list of the various types:

Nigiri-sushi – from Tokyo; small, rectangular mounds of rice shaped by hand, with thin strips of fish laid on top.

Norimaki-sushi – the rice is rolled into a cylinder with a piece of egg, mushroom or fish in the centre and wrapped in a sheet of dried seaweed.

Kappa-maki – a variant of norimaki containing cucumber.

Chirashi-sushi – ingredients arranged over a layer of rice in a lacquered box.

Inari-sushi – rice and chopped vegetables wrapped in sweetened fried tofu.

Oshi-Sushi – from Osaka; rice pressed into shape with a wooden frame.

Very few of us will have the time or energy to make that sort of range at home, but it is easy to make delicious sushi quickly yourself without using either seaweed or marinated fish (unless you want to).

The trick is to make up a large batch of the rice and keep it in the fridge ready to whack on whatever toppings you like – just like making sandwiches. All the ingredients are available in supermarkets.

SASHIMI

Now we come to the off-putting bit of Japanese cooking – the not cooking! Or not to put too fine a point on it: raw fish. Proper sashimi is transparently thin slices of the very highest quality of fish which are salted and rinsed before serving either alone or with a little cold boiled rice.

Should this not sound unappetising enough, to put you off still further, the greatest sashimi delicacy of all is made from a fish called the globefish ("fugu" in Japanese) which is, yes, you've guessed it, poisonous. Some bits of the globefish's body don't have poison in them, and these are the bits the Japanese eat if they can afford it. Very occasionally a little of the poison seeps into the supposedly edible part of the fish, and then the dish can be deadly. Fortunately globefish is not widely available in this country, and you are strongly advised to leave it well alone.

In fact raw fish is not an element of this diet at all. Recipes are given for marinating and lightly cooking your fish, but you can complete the whole diet perfectly happily without ever having to bother with raw fish.

Once you are used to eating the very lightly cooked foods common in Japanese cookery, you may well become more adventurous and feel like trying fish which has only been marinated or salted and not cooked. Interestingly enough, once you do give it a try you will find that you can't tell the fish is raw at all. In fact, if you were cheekily to serve it up to someone as smoked salmon or gravadlax they would be very unlikely to spot what you had done. In case you do want to give it a try there are two versions on page 150.

TERIYAKI

Teriyaki dishes are very popular not just in Japan but all over the world. The chances are that if you have eaten in an Oriental restaurant you will have had teriyaki beef. And you are very likely to have eaten teriyaki-flavoured meats and even teriyaki-flavoured snacks.

Essentially teriyaki is meat of the highest quality which is marinated and then cooked very quickly in either a shallow frying pan or under the grill – or even on a hot plate at your table in some Japanese restaurants. Teriyaki sauce is easily obtainable in most supermarkets and just sprinkling it on meat while you are cooking will give an instant teriyaki flavour to a dish. But for the real thing, and if you have a little time, make your own teriyaki marinade using one of the recipes given below.

When you are making a teriyaki it is important that the meat

83

is good quality so that it will be delicious even after a very short cooking time, and it often helps to cut it up into small pieces. The meats most usually served teriyaki-style are fillet steak and chicken breast, but you can be imaginative and use all sorts of meats. Why not try steaks cut from a turkey breast, or pork fillet? The "flash-fry" cut available at most supermarkets is also very suitable and not too expensive.

TABLE-TOP COOKING
One of the things that makes Japanese eating such fun, apart from it being healthy and slimming, is that the meals and the cooking styles are exciting in themselves. Instead of boring old meat and two veg, you have a whole assortment of delicious little snacky things served together. It's rather like having party food for every single meal. Better still is the fact that very often the food is actually cooked at the table, by the diners themselves. It makes the cooking part of the meal, adds to the fun, and relieves the cook of the household from having to do all the work herself (or himself). Here are details of the main styles of table-top cooking, together with advice on how to recreate them yourself at home.

Equipment:
For table-top cooking use the spirit burner and dish provided in fondue sets and other table-top cooking kits. If cooking on the hob all you need is a good heavy flameproof pot. If desired you can use chopsticks, otherwise you will need a slotted spoon to pick out the cooked delicacies from the cooking stock or oil. For table-top cooking, lay the table as follows. Put the table-top cooker in the centre of the table, not too close to any of the table settings, and with a heatproof mat underneath it. If you are going to take charge of the table-top cooking (for example if there will be young children at the table), then put the burner in front of you. Also in the centre of the table (or near your place) put the various ingredients ready to cook. Each individual place setting should include a bowl for eating from, chopsticks or forks, a soup spoon, and a small individual bowl for garnishes.

TABLE-TOP SUKIYAKI

We have the Meiji Emperor of Japan himself to thank for what is probably the most famous and popular of all Japanese dishes. He declared at the turn of the century that the Buddhist prohibition of meat eating was irrational and so opened the way for people to eat beef fillet – the major ingredient of sukiyaki. In fact sukiyaki remains a special occasion meal in Japan, and to have it on the Japanese Diet certainly turns slimming into a special occasion.

You should use the best sirloin you can afford, cut into wafer-thin slices (use the flash-fry cut as an alternative). You will need a shallow cast iron pan and a table-top cooker – yes; that old fondue set can come into its own. The thin-sliced beef and other ingredients are arranged on plates on the table and added one at a time to the pan which contains a special stock. Apart from the beef, bean curd, sliced salad vegetables, bamboo shoots and part-cooked noodles are included in the ingredients – but the exact selection is up to you to choose. Each person takes a piece at a time from the pan with chopsticks and dips the food in a small bowl of beaten egg before eating. See recipe on page 151.

TABLE-TOP TEMPURA

Like many of Japan's most exciting dishes, tempura actually owes its origins to foreign influence. It is a version of a dish brought to the Japanese by sixteenth century Portuguese traders (remember the film *Shogun*?) The name comes from "tempora" (Latin for "times") and refers to the period when the Catholic Portuguese were not allowed by their religion to eat meat and so invented this fun battered fish and seafood meal.

It has been a big favourite with the Japanese ever since and tempura restaurants are booming both here and in Japan. The traditional Japanese tempura restaurant would have low tables placed on rush "tatami" mats, with wooden sliding doors and a dark blue curtain or "noren" with the Japanese characters for tempura painted on it in white.

While you won't want to go to quite those lengths, tempura is probably the best Japanese meal for a dinner party or family meal

— the ingredients are delicious and the cooking method is a real ice-breaker. The major part of a tempura meal is usually prawns, along with a range of fish, seafood and salad vegetables. Each ingredient is individually dipped in a delicious light coating batter and then deep-fried at the table. A step-by-step guide to doing your own tempura is given on page 155 — remember you will need a table-top cooking set. You can buy specially designed tempura sets in most cook shops and Oriental stores, but any table-top cooking set will do equally well.

TABLE-TOP TEPPAN YAKI

Although only a very recent addition to Japanese cuisine (since the Second World War) teppan yaki cooking has become so popular so quickly that dishes like yaki tori chicken are practically synonymous with Japanese cooking. You can now find teppan yaki restaurants all over the world. The style of cooking gets its name from the "teppan", a cast iron plate or griddle which holds its heat so well that it can be cooked on for some time after it has been removed from a source of heat.

Japanese teppan griddles are now very high-tech electric affairs, but in China and Hong Kong the teppans are still heated up in a stove or on a range before being brought to the table, where they are rested on a special wooden tray to prevent them burning the table. You can find these old-fashioned teppans in many Chinese stores and some Western kitchen stores. If you can get hold of one, it is well worth experimenting with it since it is also very useful to use as a griddle when cooking Western-style meals — it is fantastic for steak for example.

The modern Japanese versions are either electrically heated table-top pans or little mini-grills. In some yaki dishes the heat comes from above (grilling) as in yaki tori chicken, whereas in true teppan yaki dishes, the heat source is from below from a hot plate — but the end result is surprisingly similar either way.

There is a huge variety of teppan yaki dishes. It is rather like a Western barbecue — the cooking method is so flexible that it becomes one of those free-for-alls where everybody just gets their favourite food and throws it on to cook. Here is a basic teppan method which will work with chicken, beef, pork, and vegetables.

1. Cut the meat into bite size pieces and thread onto a skewer.
2. Make up a basting mix of equal parts Soya sauce and sweet sherry with Hoisin sauce or honey added to taste.
3. Coat the skewered meat with the baste and cook briefly on both sides.
4. Brush it again with the baste and cook again briefly on both sides.
5. Keep repeating this process until the meat is cooked to your taste – it may not take very long.

LUNCH BOX OR "BENTO"

The key to a perfect Japanese "lunch box" meal is the lunch box itself, so that's where we'll start. The Japanese lunch box, called a bento, is a beautiful decorated lacquer box separated inside into a number of different food compartments. The best ones are extremely collectable. You can buy them in the West at shops like Neal Street East (see Where to Buy section pages 48–49). More workday versions are made in plastic or metal. They have compartments for each of the different lunch snacks and an airtight lid.

For serving a Bento at home you can use a shallow bread basket or even a tea tray. For a really practical Bento box to take to work with you, just use an ordinary plastic sandwich box – boring I know, but it'll do until you've really turned Japanese! Instead of compartments, use aluminium baking foil to separate the different ingredients. In fact the best Bento boxes are really too beautiful just for eating from and you may have seen them being used for other purposes – jewellery boxes, display cases, dressing-table tidiers, etc. But in reality they are just a super smart version of our good old British packed lunch container!

Rice, which is the main staple base for lunch-box cooking, nearly always has a special, slightly larger, compartment of its own and separated from the side dishes. Meat, fish, eggs or vegetables are then neatly arranged in the remaining compartments to give the meal visual appeal. A powder made of seaweed, seasame and fish flakes (called Furiake) is often sprinkled on the rice and some form of Japanese pickles is always included.

As you can probably imagine, making up a good lunch box is something of an art in itself and rather time-consuming and complicated. If you are the sort of person who makes wonderful party food and canapés you will take to it like a spring roll to soy sauce and you'll really enjoy using your imagination. To get you started a simple Bento lunch box recipe is given on page 121.

7

FOUR WEEKS OF DAILY MENU PLANS AND SHOPPING LISTS

How to Use the Menu Planner

To give you the maximum amount of flexibility while you are on the Japanese Diet, the menu planner can be used in several different ways. There are four separate tables which each cover one week, giving breakfast, lunch and dinner menus for every day. To start with it is a good idea to stick to the weekly plans since they have been carefully chosen to ensure the best balance of foods and nutrients. Later on, when you are more used to Japanese-style eating, you can move away from the weekly plans and make your own choice of breakfast, lunch and dinner each day. To help you do this, breakfasts, lunches and dinners are each described under their own section. For each dish there is a page reference for the recipe, so you can find it easily when you are ready to cook.

BREAKFASTS

Traditional Japanese breakfast is very far from what we would recognise as breakfast in the West. Its name in Japanese is "ichi-ju-issai" which literally means rice with soup and a side dish – and that's exactly what it is! Not to our taste at all – and indeed not to modern Japanese taste either. Less than 50 per cent of the Japanese continue to eat a traditional breakfast regularly.

Most Japanese now behave like busy people the world over and rush out on their daily business without even thinking of breakfast. Tokyo office workers often pick something up on their way into work – just like London commuters – but the old-fashioned Japanese breakfast is as much a thing of the past as kippers and devilled kidneys are in Britain.

To take this into account I have devised a week's worth of special modern breakfast menus which combine the best of Japanese and British breakfast ideas, at the same time as being quick to prepare, easy to digest and giving an extra-healthy start to the day. It is very important that you make time to start each day with one of these choices and don't let yourself skip breakfast. The ingredients of the breakfast recipes are particularly high in vitamins (mainly from fruit) and are very important to ensure that you get the recommended high fresh fruit intake in your diet for cancer and heart disease prevention.

If you are slimming you should also remember that eating breakfast helps weight reduction in several ways. Since food digestion actually uses 10 per cent of the daily amount of calories you take in, getting your digestion going early in the morning means you start burning calories more quickly than if you continue to fast. Studies have also shown that eating more calories at the beginning of the day and fewer at the end can increase your metabolic rate overall. And of course, eating breakfast really does help prevent an attack of the eleven o'clock nibbles.

Make your choice each morning from the menus listed below, and when you are feeling confident invent your own breakfast ideas using the same basic ingredients. Coffee should be freshly brewed, not instant.

Monday
Hot Tokyo Omelette for one (recipe p.113); 1 cup black coffee or China tea, no milk or sugar; 1 large glass fresh juice (orange, apple, tomato, grapefruit, etc).

Tuesday

Tangerine Curd for one (recipe p.108); 1 cup black coffee or China tea, no milk or sugar; ½ glass fresh orange juice topped up with boiling water.

Wednesday

Hot Spiced Fruits for one (recipe p.108); 1 cup black coffee or China tea, no milk or sugar; 1 large glass fresh juice (orange, apple, tomato, grapefruit, etc.).

Thursday

Rice Cakes for one (recipe p.109); 1 cup black coffee or China tea, no milk or sugar; ½ glass fresh orange juice topped up with boiling water.

Friday

Bean Curd Banana for one (recipe p.110); 1 cup black coffee or China tea, no milk or sugar; ½ glass fresh orange juice topped up with boiling water.

Saturday

Chrysanthemum Fruits for one (recipe p.111); 1 cup black coffee or China tea, no milk or sugar; 1 large glass fresh juice (orange, apple, tomato, grapefruit, etc).

Sunday

Fruit Cakes for one (recipe p.110); 1 cup black coffee or China tea, no milk or sugar; ½ glass fresh orange juice topped up with boiling water.

Extras During the Day

Since the Japanese Diet is not a calorie-controlled diet, you can eat as much as you like – including between meals. However, as we have discovered already, the particular foods eaten on the diet are important — more important than how much you eat. This means that you must stick to the basic Japanese foods if you want to browse between meals. The diet isn't going to help your health or slimming at all if you stuff in the jam doughnuts in between each healthy meal. In fact it is very unlikely that you will be hungry between meals on this diet, but in case you are a habitual browser, here is a list of recommended nibbles and snacks:

○ Rice cakes spread with Marmite.
○ Any fruit.
○ Cup of clear soup (see Japanese soup recipes).
○ Fresh raw slices of vegetables (crudités).
○ Japanese rice crackers.

Drinks During the Day

○ **Coffee/tea** It is important to limit your intake of coffee during the day. Try to stick to just one or two cups of fresh, not instant, coffee during the morning. Drink no coffee or other caffeine drink from afternoon onwards. Replace English tea with China tea and allow yourself two or three cups during the day.
○ **Soft drinks** Drink as much mineral water and fresh fruit or vegetable juices as you want. Decrease the amount of soft drinks and colas.
○ **Alcohol** Try to avoid any alcohol during weekday evenings, but allow yourself two or three glasses of wine on weekend evenings. Avoid spirits.

LUNCHES

As in the West, convenience is at a premium for the Japanese when it comes to lunch time. The typical lunch time meal would be fried rice (called "cha-han" in Japanese) with a salad and a cup of instant clear soup (Japanese instant soup mixes are available from Oriental grocers).

Those eating at home often end up serving dishes made from leftovers. Japanese cooking, with a variety of dishes served at dinner which can be eaten hot or cold, certainly lends itself to the left-over school of cookery. The menus given for lunch have been chosen to reflect this, with lots of quick and simple dishes.

A very special Japanese lunch time tradition is the lunch box – which is an extremely superior version of our packed lunch of sandwiches and an apple. The Japanese packed lunch includes rice, sushi, pickles, dips, seasonings and salad, all arranged in different compartments of the specially designed lunch box or Bento.

In affluent, traditional Japanese households it is the wife who gets up early each morning to make up a bento box for her husband – and even her children if they are lucky. But it is more likely that the bento will be bought take-away on the way into work or delivered from a local restaurant. Lucky London workers can copy this by buying a bento selection from a branch of Pret à Manger or having one delivered by the City restaurant Aykoku-Kaku (see page 187).

The rest of us with neither willing wives nor access to London restaurants can still join in the lunch box tradition, with a little forward planning – it is all a question of keeping the fridge stocked up. Ideas for lunch box fillings are given in the recipes section (page 121).

The Sunday lunches given below are suitable for a whole family to share since they are much more Western influenced. Otherwise, weekday meals assume you will be eating alone.

Lunches, Week One

Monday
Dash-it-off Soup (recipe p.125); 2 rice cakes spread with Marmite; mineral water or juice.

Tuesday
Japanese Lunch Box (recipe p.121). This is a complete meal in itself; China tea or mineral water.

Wednesday
Stirred Curd (recipe p.126); 2 rice cakes; 1 piece of fruit; mineral water.

Thursday
Egg Drop Soup (recipe p.115); orange; mineral water.

Friday
Mixed Bean Salad (recipe p.114); 1 piece of fruit; mineral water or China tea.

Saturday
Noodle Boodle Salad (recipe p.120). This is a complete meal in itself; wine from allowance.

Sunday
Sukiyaki (recipe p.151). This is intended to be a meal all the family can share. Serve fruit salad for dessert; wine from allowance.

Lunches, Week Two

Monday
Sushi (recipe p.149). Make up in advance to take to work; mineral water or China tea.

Tuesday
Sardine Special (recipe p.124); plain boiled rice; orange juice.

Wednesday
Tokyo Omelette Salad (recipe p.113); 2 rice cakes; fresh juice or China tea.

Thursday
Hot Pot Rice (recipe p.124). This is a complete meal in itself. If you have access to an electric ring, you can make it in advance and heat it up at work; plenty of China tea.

Friday
Japanese Lunch Box (recipe p.121); orange or vegetable juice.

Saturday
Hot Salty Prawn Salad (recipe p.112); boiled or fried rice; wine from allowance.

Sunday
Teriyaki Beef (recipe p.130). A good family meal. Serve with salad of dark green leaves or with normal Western-style vegetables; wine from allowance.

Lunches, Week Three

Monday
Mixed Bean Salad (recipe p.114); 1 orange; China tea.

Tuesday
Bamboo Rice (recipe p.119); 1 piece of fruit; mineral water.

Wednesday
Noodle Boodle Salad (recipe p.120), either hot or cold; mineral water.

Thursday
Japanese Lunch Box (recipe p.121); China tea.

Friday
Mussel Soup (recipe p.122); fresh fruit juice.

Saturday
Pepper Pot Peppers (recipe p.123). Serve with fried or boiled rice and if desired, Western-style vegetables; wine from allowance.

Sunday
Sesame Beef (recipe p.129). A good meal for the whole family to enjoy. Serve with fried or boiled rice and either a mixed salad or Western-style vegetables; wine from allowance.

Lunches, Week Four

Monday
Japanese Lunch Box (recipe p.121); 1 orange; mineral water.

Tuesday
Mushroom Salad (recipe p.111). Serve hot or cold with hot or cold rice if desired; fruit juice.

Wednesday
Miso Soup (recipe p.127). Although the full recipe for miso soup is included in the recipe section, it is simplest to use the instant sachets available in Japanese and Oriental supermarkets (see Where to Buy section). This soup makes up easily with boiling water so you can take

it into the office with you. Eat with a salad of your choice and mineral water.

Thursday
Tokyo Omelette (recipe p.113); green salad of spinach or spring greens with vinaigrette dressing; mineral water.

Friday
Fish Marinade (recipe p.116). This is a complete meal in itself. Serve hot or cold; fruit juice.

Saturday
Zen Vegetables (recipe p.118) Serve with boiled rice if desired; wine from allowance.

Sunday
Beef Rolls (recipe p.128). An ideal family Sunday lunch. Serve with boiled or fried rice and salad or Western-style vegetables; wine from allowance.

DINNERS

As in the West, the Japanese regard dinner as the main meal of the day. They tend to spend more time over its preparation and include a greater variety of dishes, although separate courses are not emphasised.

The traditional Japanese family dinner used to consist of rice, soup and three side dishes of fish, vegetables or sometimes meat. The evening meals given here have been adapted to take into account Western tastes and are designed to be served much more as we would a Western-style meal.

In fact this is fairly true in modern Japan which is now open to a wide degree of food influence from all over the world. The Japanese have no reservations about mixing the styles of food for the evening meal, and Japanese, Chinese or Western dishes are often eaten in combination. Only occasionally are desserts listed on the menus. It is very unusual to have desserts in Japan. You can treat yourself once in a while or when you are entertaining, but it is important to keep this as a rare treat if you want to get the most out of the diet.

Dinners, Week One

Monday
Mackerel Grill (recipe p.131); plain boiled rice; salad of spring greens, spring onions and tomatoes in a vinaigrette dressing; **Chrysanthemum Fruits** (recipe p.111); mineral water; China tea.

Tuesday
Simple Stir-Fry (recipe p.148). This is a complete meal in itself. For dessert, 1 orange segmented and dusted with cinnamon. Mineral water; China tea.

Wednesday
Chestnut Rice (recipe p.138); salad of raw (blanched) onion rings and sliced cucumber in a vinaigrette sauce, or with Western-style vegetables if preferred; mineral water.

Thursday
Geisha Grill (recipe p.142); plain boiled rice; selection of Western-style vegetables; mineral water.

Friday
Singapore Noodles (recipe p.142). This is a complete meal in itself. For dessert, **Tangerine Curd** (recipe p.108); mineral water.

Saturday
Tempura Party (recipe p.155). This dish has been specially chosen so that you can entertain at home while still sticking to the diet. You will find most people are delighted to join in a tempura party; wine from allowance.

Sunday
Rice and Fish Salad (recipe p.131). A light meal after a larger lunch; wine from allowance.

Dinners, Week Two

Monday
Mussel Salad (Warm) (recipe p.132). This is a light meal in itself. For dessert, fruit salad; mineral water.

Tuesday
Japanese Risotto (recipe p.139). Make any size you want and serve as a complete meal in itself; mineral water.

Wednesday
Bamboo Prawns (recipe p.133); plain boiled rice; Chinese leaves lightly dressed in sesame oil; mineral water.

Thursday
Teppan Bean Curd (recipe p.144); either Western-style vegetables or nori seaweed; mineral water.

Friday
Soya Sole (recipe p.134); plain boiled rice; shredded cabbage boiled or steamed; mineral water.

Saturday
Sesame Beef (recipe p.129). A good meal for sharing with others – either guests or family. Serve with fried rice or noodles and steamed shredded spring greens; wine from allowance.

Sunday
Sushi (recipe p.148). Sunday afternoon is a good time for making a batch of sushi to last until midweek, so having it for supper saves time; wine from allowance.

Dinners, Week Three

Monday
Shiitake Noodles (recipe p.139). This is a complete meal in itself; mineral water.

Tuesday
Grilled Trout (recipe p.135). Serve on a bed of plain boiled rice with an accompaniment of stewed tomatoes (canned will do); mineral water.

Wednesday
Seaweed Rice (recipe p.140). If dieting strictly, eat on its own. Otherwise add a large mixed salad of your choice; mineral water.

Thursday
Sake Salmon (recipe p.135); fried or boiled rice and a spring greens salad; mineral water.

Friday
Chicken Teriyaki (recipe p.145). Another Western-influenced dish that everyone will enjoy. Serve with any Western-style vegetables – even potatoes! Fruit juice.

Saturday
Sukiyaki (recipe p.151). Very much a party dish for the Japanese, and so included here as a Saturday night treat; wine from allowance.

Sunday
Sunday Rice (recipe p.141). This is a complete leftovers meal in itself; wine from allowance.

Dinners, Week Four

Monday
Wine Stew (recipe p.136); plain boiled or fried rice; puréed carrots and grilled tomatoes; mineral water.

Tuesday
Yaki Tori Chicken (recipe p.145); a large mixed salad of your choice (mayonnaise if desired) and rice if desired; mineral water.

Wednesday
Asian Rolls (recipe p.146); serve with prawn crackers, rice or Chinese pancakes. For dessert, sprinkle orange segments with cinnamon; mineral water.

Thursday
Salty Fish (recipe p.137); **Sunday Rice** (recipe p.141); a salad of spring greens or nori seaweed; mineral water.

Friday
Hot Prawn Salad (recipe p.112); plain boiled rice. For dessert, **Tangerine Curd** (recipe p.108); wine from allowance.

Saturday
Teppan Hot-Plate Party (see Cooking Methods section, page 86 recipe p.144). A traditional Oriental party meal

for you to share with your friends. For dessert, serve a selection of fruits, including exotic fruits, ready cut into segments and slightly chilled; wine from allowance; China tea.

Sunday
Pickles Rice Pick (recipe p.143). For dessert, chilled version of **Hot Spiced Fruits** (recipe p.108); china tea.

WEEKLY MENUS AT A GLANCE

Week One

	Lunch	Dinner
Monday	Dash-it-off Soup	Mackerel Grill
Tuesday	Japanese Lunch Box	Simple Stir-Fry
Wednesday	Stirred Curd	Chestnut Rice
Thursday	Egg Drop Soup	Geisha Grill
Friday	Mixed Bean Salad	Singapore Noodles
Saturday	Noodle Boodle Salad	Tempura Party
Sunday	Sukiyaki	Rice and Fish Salad

Week Two

	Lunch	Dinner
Monday	Sushi	Mussel Salad (Warm)
Tuesday	Sardine Special	Japanese Risotto
Wednesday	Tokyo Omelette Salad	Bamboo Prawns
Thursday	Hot Pot Rice	Teppan Bean Curd
Friday	Japanese Lunch Box	Soya Sole
Saturday	Hot Prawn Salad	Sesame Beef
Sunday	Teriyaki Beef	Sushi

Week Three

	Lunch	Dinner
Monday	Mixed Bean Salad	Shiitake Noodles
Tuesday	Bamboo Rice	Grilled Trout
Wednesday	Noodle Boodle Salad	Seaweed Rice
Thursday	Japanese Lunch Box	Sake Salmon
Friday	Mussel Soup	Chicken Teriyaki
Saturday	Pepper Pot Peppers	Sukiyaki
Sunday	Sesame Beef	Sunday Rice

Week Four

	Lunch	Dinner
Monday	Japanese Lunch Box	Wine Stew
Tuesday	Mushroom Salad	Yaki Tori Chicken
Wednesday	Miso Soup	Asian Rolls
Thursday	Tokyo Omelette	Salty Fish
Friday	Fish Marinade	Hot Prawn Salad
Saturday	Zen Vegetables	Teppan Hot-Plate Party
Sunday	Beef Rolls	Pickles Rice Pick

SHOPPING LISTS

To make it as easy as possible for you to get started on the Japanese Diet, four full weeks of shopping lists are printed here which you can either tear out or photocopy and take with you shopping. The list for week one is especially long because you will be stocking up your store cupboard with all the extra sauces and seasonings you need on the diet – but these will last for ages, so it's really only a one-off buy. After that, the lists are really little different from a normal weekly shopping list – plenty of fresh fruit and vegetables plus meat and fish. You may well want to buy your meat and fish fresh on the day you are going to cook it. For a guideline on specific quantities, check out the individual recipe you want to make, otherwise for general purchases like tangerines you can make your own decision on amounts, since only you know how many people you have to feed for the week. You may find you have a great many of the store cupboard purchases already in your kitchen, so just cross them off the list.

Shopping List Week One

Fresh fruit and veg:

tangerines
2–3 bananas
fresh orange juice
spring onions
root ginger
carrots
cucumber
lunch of radishes (Japanese
   if possible)
bulb of garlic
tomatoes
bunch of watercress
mushrooms
fresh spinach
fresh coriander
onions
capiscums (peppers)
Chinese leaves
celery
French beans (fresh or
   frozen)
peas (fresh or frozen)
spring greens
sugar snap peas
   (mangetout)
cauliflower
parsley

Other fresh foods:

3–4 packs bean curd
eggs
steak
mackerel fillet
chicken breast and liver
prawns (fresh frozen or
   tinned)
salmon fillet
small quantity smoked
   salmon for lunch box
   (if desired)
fish and seafood for
   tempura
eggs

For the store cupboard:

2 kg/4lb short grain rice
2 cans bamboo shoots
sesame seeds
1 large packet mixed dried
   fruits
mixed spices or five spice
   powder
1 packet rice cakes
1 small jar crystallised stem
   ginger
1 packet sunflower seed
   kernels
mixed chopped nuts
1 small tin of tuna
soya cooking oil
several packets Oriental
   soup mix
1 can mixed beans
1 can broad beans
Worcester sauce
stock cubes
1 can mixed beans
honey
olive oil
brown sugar
1 bottle of soy sauce
   (Japanese preferably)
1 bottle of sake (or cooking
   sherry)
1–2 packets dried nori
   seaweed (optional)
3 large packs cellophane
   noodles
wine vinegar
sesame oil
1 small jar pickled cockles
   or mussels
2 tins off consomme
1 jar horseradish sauce
1 bottle of Teriyaki sauce
1 tin or ½ kg/1 lb
   chestnuts
3 large packs dried noodles

Shopping List Week Two

Fresh fruit and veg:	Other fresh foods:	For the store cupboard:
new potatoes	mussels (green-lipped if possible)	brown sugar
bunch of parsley	fresh sardines	dried mushrooms
whole lemon	large prawns with shells on	large tin mussels
spring greens	beef	plum sauce
salad stuff (lettuce, spinach)	2–3 packs bean curd	pickled cockles
fresh fruit (tangerines)	sole fillets	tomato paste
green beans	steak	paprika
coriander	frozen prawns and/or shrimps	1 tin soya beans
	mackerel fillet	1 tin bamboo shoots

Shopping List Week Three

Fresh fruit and veg:	Other fresh foods:	For the store cupboard:
fresh fruit (tangerines) and vegetables (spinach, peas, watercress, horseradish, spring greens, green beans)	fresh trout	fresh (or dried) shiitake mushrooms
salad stuff	fresh salmon	dried noodles
peppers (capiscums)	chicken breasts	1 can mixed beans
parsley	mussels (green-lipped if possible)	
	steak	
	eggs	
	2–3 packs bean curd	
	pork fillet	
	mackerel fillet	

Shopping List Week Four

Fresh fruit and veg:	Other fresh foods:	For the store cupboard:
fresh shiitake mushrooms	chicken breasts	1 large jar of pickled cabbage
fresh fruit and vegetables (chives, parsley, leeks, lettuce, peas, tangerines)	eggs	1 small tin crab meat
	beef	1 can Chinese mushrooms
	mackerel fillet	1 can butter beans
	2–3 packs bean curd	1 can pineapple chunks
	herrings	
	prawns	
	minced pork	

8

RECIPES

Note on Measurements and Quantities

Japanese cooking, like other quick and Oriental cooking, is not a precise art, and more often a matter of instinct. No experienced Japanese cook, whether housewife or chef, would ever bother to weigh or measure their ingredients. A teaspoon of olive oil would be a glug poured from the bottle. So many grammes/ounces of rice would be measured purely by eye. To get into the true spirit of Japanese eating, try to adopt this method yourself – but to begin with you will need guidance about quantities, so measurements are given in both metric and imperial. All spoon measurements should be regarded as level, but you don't have to be precision accurate. Bean curd sold by the pack in the major supermarket chains is sold in 285g/10oz packs, and this is the size of pack referred to unless otherwise stated. Where cans (tins) are mentioned the average size stocked by supermarkets is approx 410–420g/a little over 14oz. The usual small can size (used for water chestnuts etc) is about 227g/7½oz. Large cans are about 500g/18oz. Again, these are the sizes referred to unless otherwise stated. References to cups assume 8ozs/250gm for solid ingredients and 10 fl oz/300ml for liquids, the average capacity of a large breakfast coffee or tea cup (unless otherwise stated). Metric/imperial equivalents are approximately: 125g/4oz; 250g/8oz; 350g/12oz; 450g/1lb.

BREAKFASTS

Tangerine Curd

Tangerines are a favourite fruit for the Japanese, and just as in Britain, they are very much a winter treat, brightening up food presentation and displayed in bowls round the house. Tangerines, satsumas and other citrus fruits are also depicted a great deal in Oriental arts and crafts, featuring in silk paintings and porcelain decoration.

So by starting your day with Tangerine Curd you are joining an ancient tradition – why not go ultra-cultural and serve your breakfast on an old decorated china dish? There are lots of lovely single dishes to be found cheaply in junk shops. If you aren't feeling so Oriental, you can substitute plain, natural set yoghurt for the bean curd.

Ingredients:
1/2 pack bean curd, drained; 2 tangerines (or satsumas); 1 tsp brown sugar; 1/2 tsp sesame seeds.

METHOD:
Slice bean curd thinly. Segment the tangerines. Arrange the bean curd and tangerines on a plate and sprinkle with sugar and sesame seeds. For variety reserve a little of the tangerine peel and shred with a sharp knife; sprinkle shreds over plate. Another variation is to heat gently 2 tsp marmalade or honey and when they are runny, pour over the top of the curd and tangerine.

Serves 1.

Hot Spiced Fruits

Preserved fruits are a celebration food in Japan, with candied or spiced plums being a favourite. If you can get hold of these (from a local delicatessen or Oriental supermarket) they make a lovely start to the day, but like the crystallised, candied and preserved fruits we eat at Christmas they can be quite rich – and expensive! This recipe captures the idea of the spicy special fruits as well as creating a warming, healthy start to a winter's morning.

Ingredients:

½–1 cup mixed dried fruit (apples, apricots, prunes, figs); un-sweetened orange juice; ½ tsp mixed spices (cinnamon, nutmeg, allspice, cloves – whatever you like).

METHOD:
Put the dried fruit in a pan with enough orange juice to cover completely. Bring to a gentle simmer. Sprinkle on the spices and stir gently while the dried fruit swells (5–10 minutes). Serve when most of orange juice has been absorbed. Some supermarkets sell ready spiced dried fruit mixes which are already part-soaked, which saves a lot of time and makes an excellent nibble food.

Serves 1.

Rice Cakes

Rice cakes are the Japanese version of crispbread. When they first started coming into Britain a few years ago, most people were very suspicious of them – partly because they look rather like expanded polystyrene (the stuff they make drinks cups from). But when people tasted them, and discovered how healthy they are, all that changed and now all the supermarkets stock them. I suppose when you think of it, our beloved potato isn't an object of great beauty either!

Ingredients:

2–4 rice cakes; select topping to taste, from: honey, crystallised stem ginger, curd cheese, bean curd, miso paste.

METHOD:
Basically whack what you want on top of your rice cake, but my favourite, and the most authentically Oriental, is to make a spread of crystallised stem ginger (available bottled in supermarkets and delicatessens) mixed with either curd cheese or mashed bean curd.
 Serves 1.

Bean Curd Banana

The great thing about bean curd is its versatility. Like plain yoghurt, it isn't the greatest thing on its own, but it takes on the most wonderful flavours when used as a recipe ingredient. It has the capacity to be either sweet or savoury, and of course has tremendous health-giving properties.

Ingredients:
1 banana; ½ pack bean curd, drained; 1 tsp chopped nuts (almonds, walnuts, hazelnuts, etc).

METHOD:
Mash up banana and bean curd together and sprinkle with chopped nuts.
 Serves 1.

Fruit Cakes

This recipe combines principles from two other breakfast recipes to make a delicious filling start to a big day.

Ingredients:
½–1 cup mixed dried fruit (apples, apricots, prunes, figs); unsweetened orange juice; ½ tsp mixed spices (cinnamon, nutmeg, allspice, cloves – whatever you like); 2–4 rice cakes; curd cheese or bean curd.

METHOD:
Prepare dried fruit as for Hot Spiced Fruits recipe. Spread rice cakes thickly with either curd cheese or thin slices of bean curd. Place rice cakes on shallow dish and spoon fruit mix over the top.
   Serves 1.

Chrysanthemum Fruits

This breakfast dish gets its name from the imperial symbol of Japan, the chrysanthemum. It is very simple to make, and if you don't feel like being very Oriental first thing in the morning you can get the same effect if you substitute yoghurt for the bean curd. All the ingredients are available from supermarkets, delicatessens and local Chinatowns.

Ingredients:
1/2 pack bean curd, drained; 1 piece fruit (preferably nectarine); 1 packet tropical mix, pumpkin or sunflower seeds.

METHOD:
Mash the bean curd into a cereal bowl. Slice the fruit and arrange into a petalled shape on top of the curd. Sprinkle with tropical mix or pumpkin or sunflower seeds to taste.
   Serves 1.

LUNCHES

Mushroom Salad

Of all nations in the world, in Britain we have the most limited view of what a salad should be. The classic British salad of two damp lettuce leaves, half a tomato and a grey slice of hard-boiled egg has done more than anything to damage the image of salads in the eyes of slimmers and, it has to be said, most men! In fact salads are the most wonderful versatile dish – warm or cold; vegetarian or meaty – and in the past we used to be as good at them as anyone, with the magnificent salmagundi as our party piece. The Japanese make some of the most unusual and delicately flavoured of all salads, so why not get started and make Britain a great salad nation again?

Ingredients:
1 tsp sesame oil; at least 1 variety fresh mushroom (preferably shiitake and oyster), sliced, 2 cups; 4 spring onions (or young small leeks), in slivers; 8 sprigs watercress; 1 tsp lemon juice; 2 tsp Japanese or light soy sauce; 1 tsp sake or any kind of sherry; dashi stock.

METHOD:
Heat the oil in a deep frying pan. Add sliced mushrooms and sauté very gently until shiny and becoming soft. Remove mushrooms and place in serving dish. Add spring onions and fry quickly, removing from pan while still crisp; add to serving dish along with watercress. Remove pan from heat and add lemon juice, soy sauce and sake to pan juices, blending together as the pan cools down. This is going to be your dressing, so estimate how much liquid you will need to coat everything thoroughly. Add stock as necessary. Pour the still cooling liquid over the salad and toss everything until it is all well mixed. You can serve this salad warm or cold. If you want to use it as a starter to impress guests, serve it warm – this is the big fashion in trendy London restaurants and costs a fortune!

Serves 2.

Hot Salty Prawn Salad

Like most of the lunch dishes here, this one can easily double up as a starter for dinner, or even a light main course. I've included it for lunch because its spiciness makes a great pick-me-up in the middle of the day. The quantities can be varied depending on how many you want to feed and for what meal. I generally allow three large prawns each for a light lunch or starter.

The combination of warm and cold in the salad is delicious. Provide a finger bowl and a spare dish for people to put their prawn heads and shells into – although the shells are so delicious I've known people to eat them as well!

Ingredients:

6 tbsp soy sauce; 1/2 tsp horseradish sauce; 1 sugar-lump size piece fresh root ginger, chopped (or crystallised stem ginger for a sweeter taste); 6 large cooked prawns with shell; soya oil; sea salt; fresh baby spinach leaves; fresh lettuce leaves; 1 tomato, chopped.

METHOD:

First prepare the dressing by mixing together the soy sauce, horseradish and ginger. Put to one side. Thread the prawns onto skewers (three per skewer) and lay on a baking tray. Brush with oil and sprinkle with sea salt. Put under a medium grill where they will begin to char (this doesn't take very long so keep an eye on them). Tear the spinach and lettuce leaves roughly into a large salad bowl with the tomato. Turn the prawns over and do other side. When the prawns are ready, use a fork to pull them off the skewers and onto the leaves in the salad bowl. Pour the dressing over the top and serve.

Serves 2.

Tokyo Omelette (Hot or as a Salad)

This Japanese fast food has a huge variety of uses. You can put it on top of sushi, or in soups. You can use it cold as a salad garnish or you can eat it hot as a main course. It's also a dish that will keep pretty well in the fridge. If you want Hot Tokyo Omelette, just serve it immediately you have finished preparing it, and don't bother to slice it into thin sections. For a Tokyo Omelette Salad, make up your normal green salad with a vinaigrette dressing and use one omelette, sliced thin, per person.

Ingredients:

6 eggs; 6 tbsp dashi stock; 2 tsp sweet sherry; 1½ tbsp any kind of sugar; 2 tsp cornflour; salt to taste; soya oil.

METHOD:

Beat together all the ingredients except the oil. Heat a trace of oil in a large non-stick frying pan. Pour enough batter in to cover, as though you were going to make a pancake. Once the thin omelette is cooked firm, roll it up to the edge of the pan. Repeat the process, rolling the next omelette round the outside of the first one, so that you are gradually building up a long, fat omelette sausage with many layers. When your first omelette sausage is about 1½ inches (4 cm) across, transfer it to a plate and keep warm while you finish the mixture.

This is how the Japanese do it, but if you find it tricky, then you can make your thin omlettes individually and stack them one on top of the other on a plate before rolling. The effect isn't quite as effective but still tastes good.

Finally, slice the omelette sausages and serve with salad or with Mixed Bean Salad (below). Or keep and use them as described above.

Serves 4–6 used as garnish or breakfast.

Mixed Bean Salad

There are two ways of doing this. The complicated way is by soaking dried soya beans and cooking them. The easy way is by getting a can of ready to eat soya beans from your local supermarket (most supermarkets have them, but Safeway's are particularly good). I'm going to assume you want to do it the easy way.

Ingredients:

1 can soya beans (ready to eat); ½ can mung or broad beans (ready to eat); 5 tsp cucumber, finely chopped; 1 tbsp English or Japanese daikon radish, finely chopped; 4 spring onions, finely chopped; 1 tsp crystallised stem ginger; 1 tbsp minced garlic; 1 tbsp Japanese

sauce; 1 tbsp soy sauce; 1 tbsp any kind of sherry (or sake); 1 tbsp runny honey.

METHOD:
Drain the cans of beans and mix together in a bowl (be gentle, otherwise you will break up the beans too much). Add the cucumber, radish and spring onion and toss together. In a separate bowl mix the remaining ingredients well and pour over the beans. Toss only briefly and serve.

Serves 2 large portions.

Egg Drop Soup

This soup is such a staple of Oriental cuisine that it is hard to work out whether it was originally Chinese, Japanese or what. Its simplicity and delicate flavouring make me suspect that it may have started life in Japan, but despite their traditional mutual dislike, the two nations have influenced each other, so who knows. By the way, a version of this soup has also made its way into the European cuisine as Consommé Celeste, and this alternative is also described below.

You can make this soup at work with even the most basic of kitchen facilities. All you need is a fridge (most offices have them to keep milk in, but you'll keep a couple of eggs in it) and a ring to heat a can of consommé. Heat the soup and stir in the egg. You can also ask any canteen or restaurant which serves clear soup to break an egg into it for you.

Ingredients:
1/2 pint (10 fl oz/300ml) consommé (canned or home-made) per person; 1 egg per person; 1 tsp soy sauce (increase if making large quantities); 1 tsp sake (increase if making large quantities).

METHOD:
Pour the consommé into a large pan and bring to a simmer. Meanwhile break the egg into a bowl and beat it with a fork until all

the white and yolk have mixed together. When the consommé is simmering gently, add the soy sauce and sake. Now pick up a forkful of beaten egg and trail it into the consommé. You will notice that it sets immediately in a thin hair-like trail. Repeat the process until all the egg is used up. While you are doing this it is important to keep the soup and your fork moving so you get the right size threads – if you slow down you get ugly lumps which aren't such a nice texture. Make sure the soup doesn't go off the simmer; if it is too cool the egg won't set quickly enough. It's not complicated when you get the hang of it, and superior British-style cooks will recognise the technique as very similar to that used for clarifying stocks. Once you have made all your egg drops, serve the soup immediately.

Serves 1.

Celeste Variation

Ingredients:
½ pint (10 fl oz/300ml) consommé (canned or home-made); 1 tsp soy sauce; 1 tsp sake; 1 cup Tokyo Omelette, thinly sliced (recipe p.113).

METHOD:
Couldn't be simpler – just heat the consommé, add the soy sauce and sake; garnish with slices of Tokyo Omelette and serve with a sprig of parsley.

Serves 1.

Fish Marinade (Sushi-style Fish)

This is perhaps the most adventurous dish on the Japanese Diet, but it really is worth getting the hang of as it's such a foundation of

Japanese cuisine and health. What is so different about this dish is the way the fish is prepared. Did you know that you can "cook" a food without heating it? Curing is one such method, as is cold smoking. Anybody who loves smoked salmon is familiar with the taste and texture of fish that has been cooked without heat – so don't switch off yet! The method described here is the marinade. Many cooks use a marinade before grilling or barbecuing foods, but the marinade alone is enough to "cook" certain foods, especially fish, and this is what we are going to do now.

Ingredients:
I mackerel fillet; marinade (see below); ½ cup short grain rice; rice sauce to taste (see below); two sheets nori, shredded; I cup green beans, chopped.
Marinade ingredients:
I tsp salt; I tsp lemon juice; 2 tbsp wine vinegar; I tbsp soy sauce.
Rice sauce ingredients:
I tbsp sake or any kind of sherry; I tbsp soy sauce; I tsp any kind of sugar; 2 tbsp vinegar; I tbsp orange juice.

METHOD:
First blanch your mackerel by pouring boiling water over it, followed immediately by very cold water. Pat dry with a paper towel. Skin the mackerel and slice in thin strips, placing them on a shallow dish.

Mix up the marinade and coat the mackerel thoroughly, turning the pieces over so the marinade is evenly spread. Cover and leave in the fridge while you boil up your rice as described on page 74. Lightly boil the beans (remember it is best to add the beans to water that is already on the boil). Mix up your rice sauce ingredients.

Now comes the really Japanese bit. Drain the rice and beans together into a serving dish and mix in the rice sauce. Remove the mackerel slices from the marinade and place on top of the hot rice. Garnish with nori shreds and serve. If you really can't face the mackerel straight from the marinade you can sear it quickly on both sides on a griddle or under the grill before you serve it.
Serves I.

Zen Vegetables

The original Japanese version of this recipe used to be prepared by monks who had little more to do with their time than contemplate the perfect meal. Should you know a Zen monk I am sure he will be able to make you the real thing and it will be delicious. For those of us with rather more down-to-earth lives this is a quicker version which I hope captures some of the delicacy and flavour of the original. By the way I have included crab meat, which the Zen monks as vegetarians would not have eaten; whether you do is up to you.

Ingredients:
2 tsp cornflour (for thickening); 2 tsp sweet sherry; 2 tsp wine vinegar; 1 tsp soy sauce; 1 tbsp sesame oil; 1 can (300g/11oz) butter beans; 1 can Chinese mushrooms (or button mushrooms); 2 tsp sesame seeds; 2 cups green beans, sliced; 1/2 cup dashi stock; 1 small tin crab meat, drained and shredded.

METHOD:
First, blend the cornflour with the sherry, vinegar and soy sauce in a jug ready to use when you want to thicken your sauce. Next heat the oil in a deep frying pan. While the oil is heating drain your cans of butter beans and mushrooms and have them ready. When the oil is hot put in the sesame seeds and the green beans and stir-fry until the beans are just beginning to soften (about 3 minutes). Add the butter beans and mushrooms. Pour on enough stock to simmer them without sticking or burning (you may not need all the stock). Keep stirring. Now toss in the shredded crab meat and keep stirring for 10–20 seconds. If you think you would like more sauce and you haven't used all your stock, now is the time to add a little more. Finally pour on the thickening mixture and stir until it has thickened and cleaned. Serve. You will find you have an unusual combination of a thick but light sauce together with crisp beans which contrast with the soft textures of the crab and mushrooms.
Serves 2.

Bamboo Rice

In Japan the fresh bamboo shoot season is awaited with as much excitement as we look forward to the arrival of the first English strawberries. The implications are much the same too, a taste of summer to come and a promise that winter won't be back for a long time. In Britain fresh bamboo shoots are few and far between (though you may find them in an Oriental supermarket) so this recipe uses tinned bamboo shoots, which I'm afraid are not as good as the real thing. If you do manage to find fresh shoots use about 250g/18oz.

Ingredients:

1 cup raw short grain rice; stock (for boiling rice); 2 onions; 1 tbsp sesame oil; 1 can bamboo shoots; 1 tbsp any kind of sherry; 1 tbsp chilli sauce; 1 tsp crystallised stem ginger, finely chopped, syrup drained.

METHOD:
Wash the rice and drain – a useful technique for this particular recipe. Put in a non-stick pan with enough stock to cover. Ideally you should use dashi stock, but a stock cube will do (in fact Knorr make stock cubes especially for cooking rice). Cover the pan and bring the rice to the boil. Simmer gently until the rice is cooked. If you have judged it right, all the stock will be absorbed but sometimes you may have to add a little water or there is a little stock left over. I'm afraid there is no fail-safe set of rice-to-liquid proportions I can give you, but once you're used to the process it won't be a problem. While the rice is cooking with the other ingredients (not forgetting to keep an eye on the rice and stir it occasionally to prevent the bottom from cooking faster than the top), slice the onion and fry in the oil until soft and just the brown side of golden. Stir in the drained bamboo shoots, the sherry, chilli sauce and ginger and keep all warm while you drain the rice onto a serving dish. Pour the bamboo shoots on top and serve.

Serves 1 for a complete snack lunch, 2 as a side dish in a larger meal.

Noodle Boodle Salad

I first came across this salad in Hong Kong where it provided the most wonderful cooling sensation in the middle of all that tropical humidity. Transparent or cellophane noodles appear in many favourite Chinese and Japanese dishes. They are now available in many supermarket chains as well as in Oriental stores and delicatessens, and they make a wonderful novelty food for children.

Ingredients:
2 tbsp Japanese soy sauce; 4 tbsp any kind of sherry; 2 tbsp wine vinegar; 1 tbsp any kind of sugar; 3 tbsp olive oil; 3 tbsp sesame oil; 6 tomatoes, chopped; 2 Japanese daikon white radishes (substitute horseradish or red radish), finely diced; 1 small head spring greens or fresh spinach, roughly shredded; 1 bundle cellophane noodles (usually come in bunches inside their wrappings); 6 strips nori, shredded (optional).

METHOD:
Put a pan of water on to boil. Meanwhile, mix the dressing – it's quickest to mix it straight into your salad bowl. So measure the soy sauce, sherry, wine vinegar, sugar and oils into the bowl. Add the tomatoes and radishes and stir it all together. By now the water should be boiling so plunge in your heap of shredded greens to give them a quick blanch. Use a wire blanching basket it you have one. They shouldn't stay in for more than a minute. Take them out either still in the basket or with a slotted spoon. Rinse them in cold water, either in a colander or still in the blanching basket. Leave to drain. Now put the cellophane noodles in the still boiling water you used for the greens – this saves time, adds flavour to the noodles and means you don't waste any precious nutrients from the vegetables. The noodles won't take long to cook (5–10 minutes), but you need to

watch and stir them the whole time so that they don't stick together. As soon as they are ready, drain them and add them to the salad bowl along with the now cool greens. Toss the whole lot thoroughly until the dressing is evenly spread. Garnish with nori shreds and serve.

Serves about 6.

Japanese Lunch Box

The lunch box meal is very much the Japanese equivalent of the British office worker's sandwich or burger-to-go, which is why I recommend it as an excellent idea for those whose day at the office is too busy to permit anything more complicated. If you work in Central London you are lucky because the sandwich chain Pret à Manger does take-away Japanese lunches but the rest of us will have to prepare our own in advance. You can be very Japanese about this and have a few perfectly presented sushi in a lacquered box, or you can make it more English by throwing a few cold ingredients in a Tupperware.

To be authentically Japanese you should include more than one dish in your lunch box collection, but without the kind of specially designed box used in Japan it can be difficult to keep everything from jumbling together. However, anyone who has ever had to provide their children with a packed lunch should possess sufficient ingenuity. For sushi recipes look on page 148. To get you started, and probably as an end point for most of us, here are some quick and simple lunch box ideas. Mainly they use leftovers or things you can keep in the fridge so that you don't have to spend too much time on elaborate preparation.

Lunch box ingredients

Main compartment: This is always for rice. Use leftover cold rice and sprinkle it with a light dressing of wine vinegar, sake and sugar. Garnish with either nori seaweed shreds or mock caviar (lumpfish roe) or grated hard boiled egg or capers or chopped gherkins. Or use rice cakes with toppings

Meat/fish compartments: Make little rolls of smoked salmon; or put in slivers of cold leftover Yaki Tori chicken; or cut up pieces of continental cured meats and sausages; or have slices of hard-boiled egg garnished with whole anchovies. Or use leftover sushi prepared and kept in fridge.

Mussel Soup

A lot of people are very put off at the idea of cooking with shellfish and other seafood, but with this recipe it is extremely simple – and you don't have to get involved with anything raw at all (unless of course you count the onion). Ideally you should use the fresh cooked green-lipped mussels which are sold on the half-shell by Waitrose and other supermarket chains. If you can't get hold of these, then substitute frozen (thaw first) or canned mussels – don't use pickled mussels as this will affect the flavour.

Ingredients:
2–3 large cloves garlic; 2 onions; I handful parsley; 2 tbsp sesame oil; 2 pints (40 fl oz/1150ml) dashi stock; I handful coriander; 2 tsp any kind of sherry; 12 green-lipped mussels on the half-shell; tabasco to taste.

METHOD:
Finely chop the garlic, onions and parsley and, using a large deep saucepan, stir-fry them in one tablespoon of the oil until the onion is soft. Pour on the dashi stock. Once it has reached a low boil add the coriander, roughly chopped, with all long, thick stalks removed as they can be tough. Add the sherry. Keeping the pan on a low simmer, put the mussels in gently one by one, still on their shells. Push each mussel down with a wooden spoon so that they are all covered. Leave to simmer gently for only about 4 or 5 minutes. Serve either into individual bowls, allowing 3 or 4 mussels per person, or into a large tureen. Dribble the remaining tablespoon of oil over the soup and a dash of tabasco if liked.
    Serves 3–4.

Pepper Pot Peppers

This is such a versatile dish that you can eat it as a filling winter lunch on its own, serve it as a starter or even make it a main course – especially if you substitute a marrow or pumpkin for the green peppers (you will have to increase the ingredients accordingly). It is also quite unusual for a Japanese dish since it uses pork. I think it may be another of those Chinese-influenced dishes since the Chinese are very fond of minced pork.

Ingredients:
4 green peppers/capsicums (halved lengthways and centres removed); 1 tbsp soya oil; 1 tsp sesame seeds; 1 small onion, finely chopped; 1 clove garlic, crushed; 225g/8oz pork fillet (not too lean), minced or blender-chopped; 1 tbsp soy sauce; 1/4 tsp chilli powder; ½ tsp mixed spice or five spice powder; 1 tbsp flour; 1 lightly beaten egg.

METHOD:
Boil a pan of water and blanch the peppers for a few minutes, taking them out while still crisp. Set to one side. Heat the oil in a deep frying pan and stir-fry the sesame seeds until they are roasted light brown; add the onion, garlic and pork and continue to stir-fry until onion is soft. Season with the soy sauce, chilli powder and spices. Sprinkle with the flour to absorb the juices and leave to cook gently on a low heat for 10 minutes. Keep an eye on it and if it looks very dry or in danger of burning add a little water. Spoon the pork mixture into the peppers and brush egg over the top. Place briefly under grill until egg has set. Serve.
   Serves 4.

Sardine Special

This is a delicious recipe but be warned – a tin of sardines is no substitute, so don't even attempt it if you can't get hold of fresh sardines. Fortunately supermarkets are much more enlightened these days and you should certainly find fresh sardines regularly on most fish counters and at the fishmongers (if you have access to such a rarity). I suggest that you don't plan to have this dish until *after* you have seen and bought some sardines!

Ingredients:
4 tbsp soy sauce; 4 tbsp wine vinegar; 2 tbsp lemon juice; I walnut-size piece of fresh root ginger, peeled and chopped; 2 cloves garlic, crushed; 4 fresh sardines; I large head spring greens, shredded; 3 tbsp soya oil.

METHOD:
Mix together the soy sauce, vinegar, lemon juice, ginger and garlic and marinade the sardines in it for 2 hours at room temperature. Turn and baste them occasionally to make sure the marinade has a chance to soak into the fish. Boil a pan of water and cook the spring greens until tender but still crisp and green. Drain into a serving dish. Drizzle with I tbsp of the oil and put in a low oven to keep warm. Remove the sardines from the marinade and grill under a high heat, basting with the remaining oil. They will take 3–4 minutes (check for eyes going opaque and skin going a golden, slightly crispy brown). Remove sardines from grill and serve on the bed of spring greens, to give the idea of fish and seaweed.

Serves 4; for I just divide ingredients by four.

Hot Pot Rice

A real fast-food dish which is popular throughout China and Japan and, since it is usually cooked and served in individual dishes, is ideal for those eating alone. The lidded china pots used for this dish are very specific to the Far East and are generally beautifully decorated. They are roughly the size and shape of a baked beans tin, with a loosely fitting lid. They originate from China, where they started out as tea cups – the lids kept the tea hot in very cold Peking winters – and gradually the custom developed of serving tasty little hot ricey snacks in them. These pots are for sale in Oriental stores and supermarkets, and they are so pretty and useful (you can serve soup in them or indeed hot drinks) that I think it is worth investing in one. However, any small heatproof ceramic (china) pot with a lid will do – try a small casserole or large cocotte dish.

Ingredients:

Enough cooked rice to fill chosen pot three quarters full; enough various leftovers eg, peas, cold meat, prawns, hard-boiled egg, to fill pot nearly to rim; 1 tsp teriyaki sauce; 1 tsp plum sauce; 1 tsp soy sauce.

METHOD:

Put rice into pot with chosen leftovers on top. Mix up the teriyaki, plum and soy sauces and pour over. Put on lid. Steam pot for 10–15 minutes. To do this you can either use a two-section steamer pan, or put an upturned dish in a pan of boiling water and place the pot on top. It doesn't matter if the base of the pot is in the water but it is important to have plenty of steam. The steaming method moistens the rice, amalgamates the flavours and brings the sauce down into the mixture.

Serves 1.

Dash-it-off Soup

I have called this Dash-it-off because not only is it quick to make, but it is also based on the traditional Japanese dashi stock. The easiest way to make dashi is by using instant dashi powder available at Tesco, selected Sainsbury's branches and Oriental supermarkets. Here I'm giving a recipe for the dashi stock which is quite quick and still has a touch of authenticity. First make the stock:

Ingredients for stock:

1 chicken stock cube; 1½ pints (30 fl oz/940ml) water; 3 or 4 strips dried seaweed (preferably kombu, but nori will do); 3 tinned

anchovies (the Japanese would use dried tuna or bonito and if you can get dried fish, by all means try it).

METHOD:
Dissolve stock cube in pan with water and add seaweed and anchovies. Allow to simmer gently for 2 minutes. Strain stock off into a jug and discard the seaweed and anchovies.

Now for the soup, which is an unusual clear fish soup based on the Japanese liking for tuna.

Ingredients for soup:
2 tsp soya oil; 2 carrots, cut into matchsticks; 6 spring onions; 2 walnut-size pieces fresh root ginger, peeled and cut into matchsticks; 100g/4oz fresh tuna, sliced, or 1 small tin of tuna; 1½ pints (30 fl oz /940ml) dashi stock.

METHOD:
Heat the oil in a saucepan and stir-fry carrots, spring onions and ginger. When the carrots begin to soften add the tuna. If you are using fresh tuna, fry it quite vigorously for a moment or two, before adding the stock. If you are using tinned tuna, it tends to fall apart quickly so add the dashi stock almost immediately. When you have added the stock, allow to simmer gently for 5 minutes and then serve.

Serves 2 as lunch main course, 4 as accompaniment for dinner main dish.

Stirred Curd

Much Japanese food is quite bland by our junk-food conditioned tastes and it is as well to realise that there will always be a conflict between healthy, light foods and rich, over-flavoured and highly processed foods. This dish is a case in point. It is good for the digestion, light and nourishing, but it may take your palate some time to become adjusted to the delicate flavouring.

Ingredients:

I bunch watercress; I tsp sesame oil; I pack bean curd drained;
I pint (20 fl oz/600ml) dashi stock (or consommé); I inch/2.5cm
piece of cucumber, cut into matchsticks.

METHOD:

Roughly chop the watercress into a saucepan and sauté in the oil
until it is glossy and wilted. Slice the bean curd thickly and put into
the pan. Turn each slice over once or twice – gently, don't let them
break up. Add the stock and simmer gently for 5 minutes. Just before
serving toss in the cucumber matchsticks.
  Serves 2.

Miso Soup

I have included this recipe because it is so authentically Japanese,
but I warn that the taste of the miso is like nothing we eat in the
West – you'll either love it or hate it! If the latter, or if you have
trouble getting hold of the miso (a paste made from ground soya
beans), then just substitute a tin of consommé.

Ingredients:

I ½ pints (30 fl oz/940ml) dashi stock; 3 tbsp miso paste (when
adjusting quantities allow I tbsp miso paste per half-pint (10 fl oz/
315ml) of dashi stock); 6 strips nori, shredded; I Tokyo Omelette,
sliced (recipe p.113).

METHOD:

Put the dashi stock in a saucepan over a moderate heat. Add the
miso paste and keep stirring until it is all evenly melted and dissolved.
Sprinkle in the nori shreds and simmer briefly for a minute or two
(not too fiercely). Garnish with the omelette slices and serve.
  *Serves 2 as lunchtime main course, 4 as dinner time accompani-
ment.*

SUNDAY LUNCHES/DINNERS

Beef Rolls

This is another dish that the whole family will like, so I have included it under the Sunday lunch heading. Obviously you can adapt your menus to take account of when your family eats together. This version of beef is really delicious, but to make it especially memorable (perhaps for a dinner party or a celebration meal) it is worth going to a butcher and asking him to prepare you some very thin slices of fillet steak – expensive but yummy. For a more day-to-day version (would that we could all dine regularly on fillet steak) I recommend using the thin flash-fry steak available in most supermarkets.

Ingredients:

1 tsp ground ginger; 500g/1lb steak, sliced thin; 6 tbsp soy sauce; 4 spring onions in slivers; 2 carrots cut into matchsticks; 4 dried mushrooms soaked until rehydrated and thinly sliced; 2 sticks celery cut into matchsticks; 4 tbsp soya oil; 4 tbsp sweet sherry; large crisp lettuce leaves.

METHOD:

Rub the ginger into the steak slices and then marinate for 20 minutes at room temperature in 2 tbsp of the soy sauce. Lay flat each slice of steak in turn and place a pinch of the other ingredients – spring onions, carrots, mushrooms and celery – in the middle of the slice. Roll up into a cigar shape and secure by piercing with a wooden cocktail stick. When all the beef rolls have been made, heat the oil in a deep frying pan and start frying the rolls leaving in the sticks to keep them closed. Put the rolls in the pan and keep turning them until they are all thoroughly browned and sealed. Now pour on the sherry and remaining soy sauce and simmer gently until the steak is cooked to your taste. The Japanese way of serving this is to put the rolls onto a dish and then let everybody wrap a roll individually in a lettuce leaf and eat it with the fingers – the lettuce leaf not only prevents the fingers getting burnt but makes a delicious contrast between the cool crisp lettuce and the hot spicy beef. Alternatively you could serve the rolls on a bed of lettuce.

Serves 4.

Sesame Beef

The crushed sesame seeds in this dish make it a great favourite with children – who usually end up eating it with their fingers. Much Japanese food has an emphasis on being fun to eat – despite the formality elsewhere in Japanese life. The use of chopsticks makes it easy for everyone to enjoy dipping into communal dishes of what we would call "finger food" – chopsticks often remind me of a hygienic version of fingers anyway. If you can't stand the thought of chopsticks, substitute a fork – and there's nothing wrong with fingers either!

Ingredients:
4 x 225g/8oz steaks.
Marinade ingredients:
1½ tbsp sesame seeds; 1 garlic clove, crushed; 2 tbsp soy sauce; 1 tbsp sake or dry sherry; 1 tsp any kind of sugar.
Dipping sauce ingredients:
2 spring onions, finely chopped; 1 inch/2.5cm piece fresh root ginger, peeled and grated; 1/2 tsp paprika; 150ml/5 fl oz soy sauce; 2 tbsp dashi stock (or substitute).

METHOD:
Start off by dry roasting the sesame seeds over the hob in a heavy bottomed pan until they turn brown and start popping. Remove them from the pan and crush them thoroughly. Now make the marinade in a large shallow dish by mixing the crushed seeds with all the other marinade ingredients. Baste the steaks thoroughly in the marinade and leave at room temperature for 30 minutes. Mix up all the dipping sauce ingredients and divide into 4 small serving bowls,

one for each place at the table. Remove the steaks from the marinade and cook under a hot grill until they are done according to your taste (the better quality the meat, the less time it needs to cook). Before serving the steaks, transfer them quickly to a chopping board and roughly slice them into strips before arranging on individual plates. Diners can use either forks, chopsticks or fingers to dip each strip of steak into the dipping sauce before eating.

Serves 4.

Teriyaki Beef

Despite their historical differences with the Japanese, Americans are very fond of the mixture of sweet and sour tastes inherent in Japanese cooking. Teriyaki sauce is a national favourite in the US, to such an extent that you can buy teriyaki flavoured potato chips (crisps) and all sorts of other snack foods which no self-respecting Japanese would be seen dead eating. Because teriyaki is becoming such a universal favourite world-wide, most supermarkets in Britain now stock teriyaki sauce/marinade alongside soy sauce on their shelves. You can use teriyaki sauce as a marinade or as a separate seasoning just like soy sauce, and of course using a ready-made version makes cooking Teriyaki Beef all the easier.

Ingredients:
125ml/4 fl oz teriyaki sauce; 1 clove garlic, crushed; 4 tbsp soft brown sugar; 1 piece crystallised stem ginger, finely chopped; 4 small, good quality steaks; soya oil.

METHOD:
Combine the teriyaki sauce, garlic, sugar and ginger for the marinade. Lay the steaks in a wide shallow dish, baste with the marinade and leave for 1 hour at room temperature. Heat the oil in a large heavy frying pan. Remove the steaks from the marinade (retaining the marinade) and seal them thoroughly in the oil until they are well browned on the outside. Drain off any excess oil or fat. Pour on

the marinade and continue to cook the steaks, turning regularly, until they are done according to your taste. Serve the steaks individually, pouring pan juices over each one.

Serves 4.

DINNERS

Mackerel Grill

This dish couldn't be simpler. I've used filleted mackerel, but if you're happy serving your fish on the bone, then feel free.

Ingredients:
4 mackerel fillets; 4 tbsp horseradish sauce; 1 handful coriander; 4 tbsp teriyaki sauce.

METHOD:
Clean the mackerel thoroughly and spread 1 tbsp of the horseradish sauce in the cavity of each fish. Divide the coriander into four and stuff the cavities with it. Brush the skin of each fish with teriyaki sauce and cook under a medium grill, turning frequently and basting with more teriyaki sauce. You will know the fish is done when the eye goes opaque (if you have left the head on) or when the flesh feels firm and the skin slightly crispy.

Serves 4.

Rice and Fish Salad

In Japan this dish would normally be prepared using raw or marinated fish as with sashimi and sushi, but I've created a version which uses cooked fish, as I think it tastes equally nice and is much more suited to the British palate. I've chosen salmon, but you could substitute more or less any fish so long as it is not too bony and has a fairly close-textured flesh – fresh tuna or swordfish is ideal. You can serve this either hot or cold.

Ingredients:
500g/1lb salmon fillet; 1 tbsp salt; 2 tsp horseradish sauce; 50ml/2 fl oz soy sauce; 2 tbsp sake or dry sherry; 450g/1lb raw short grain rice; 50ml/2 fl oz white wine vinegar; 1 tbsp any kind of sugar; 2 tbsp soya oil; 1 head spring greens, shredded.

METHOD:
Clean the fish and gently rub in the salt all over. Cover and put in the fridge while you prepare the other ingredients. Mix together the horseradish sauce, soy sauce and sake and put to one side. Cook the rice, drain into a serving bowl and stir in the wine vinegar and sugar, making sure it is all distributed thoroughly. If you are serving this as a hot salad, put the rice in a very low oven to keep warm while you cook the fish. Rinse off the fish and slice into thickish (about ½ inch/1.25cm) ribbons against the grain. Heat the oil in a heavy pan and put in the fish. Turn over quickly a couple of times until the flesh starts to change colour and then pour on the horseradish, soy and sake mix. Simmer very briefly (a couple of minutes) – most fish, especially salmon, takes no cooking at all. If you are serving this salad hot, then immediately combine the salmon, the shredded raw greens and the rice all together in the serving bowl, tossing well with any remaining cooking liquid. If you are serving it cold, then allow the various ingredients to cool before tossing and serving.

Serves 2–4 depending on appetite and whether served as a main course or dish with accompaniments.

Mussel Salad

Like most Japanese salads this can be served hot or cold, but I prefer it as a refreshing cold main course to serve in the summer. It is one of very few Japanese dishes that usespotato, and for us in Britain I think this is another reason for eating it in the summer when the new potatoes are at their best. The recipe uses tinned mussels, as serving on the shell is not a feature of this dish, but if you are going to use fresh, do make sure you don't use any that have opened before you cook them.

Ingredients:
450g/1lb small new salad potatoes, quartered; 1 large tin mussels (in brine rather than vinegar) or equivalent in fresh mussels (about 20–30); 2 tbsp soya oil; 1 garlic clove, crushed; 4 tbsp dry white wine; 1 tsp vinegar; 2 tbsp chopped parsley or chives; a few chrysanthemum flowers for the garnish (optional).

METHOD:
Boil the potatoes, making sure that they remain firm. Drain and put aside. Drain the mussels. Heat the oil in a saucepan and stir-fry the garlic. Pour on the mussels and turn them over gently a few times before adding the white wine and vinegar. Simmer for a few seconds and then remove the mussels. Toss them together in a salad bowl with the potatoes. Continue simmering the pan juices until they have reduced to a quantity sufficient to dress your salad. Pour on the juices, toss the potato and mussel salad again. Garnish with the parsley or chives and serve.

If you are using fresh mussels add some stock at the cooking stage so that they are well covered with liquid, and simmer until they are firm and cooked before continuing with the recipe. The remaining pan juices after the mussels are removed will need to be simmered for longer to reduce them.

Serves 2–4 depending on appetite.

Bamboo Prawns

With its mild and delicate flavouring, this is such a typical Japanese dish. For British palates I recommend it as a perfect Sunday supper meal or for any time when you've had rather too much spicy food and your digestion needs a bit of a rest.

Ingredients:
2 tbsp sesame oil; 400g/14oz tin bamboo shoots, drained and sliced; 2 tbsp sake; 2 tbsp sweet sherry; 2 tbsp tomato paste; 350g/12oz frozen prawns, thawed and thoroughly drained.

METHOD:
Heat the oil in a deep frying pan and add the bamboo shoots. Stir-fry for a minute or so. Stir in the sake, sherry and tomato paste until it is all thoroughly incorporated and then add the prawns. Allow to simmer for 2 minutes. Then turn contents into a dish and serve.
Serves 4.

Soya Sole

In Britain we are used to treating sole with the utmost respect. Usually it is grilled with a dab of parsley butter and a dash of lemon juice and nothing else. But its firm white flesh is in fact an ideal vehicle for a great variety of different cooking methods and flavours, and that is certainly how the Japanese use it. Here it takes on a spicy flavour which I think will be new to most of us.

Ingredients:
250ml/8 fl oz each of dashi stock (or substitute), soy sauce and sake; 3 tsp any kind of sugar; 4 fillets of sole; 2 inch/5cm piece fresh root ginger, peeled and sliced; fresh coriander.

METHOD:
Preheat a slow oven (150°C, Gas Mark 2, 300°F). Mix the sauces and sugar together in a wide deep pan big enough for the fish. Bring to the boil. Arrange the fish in the pan and sprinkle with the ginger. Bring back to a simmer and simmer for 5 minutes. Transfer fish to a warmed, ovenproof serving dish and strew with coriander. Pour

over enough liquid to cover the fish. Cover and bake in the oven for 10 minutes before serving.

Serves 4.

Grilled Trout

Miso paste is an ingredient of the authentic version of this dish. If you can get it, wonderful, but if not just leave it out of the marinade. You can also use the same recipe for mackerel, in which case I would cook it for 5 minutes longer.

Ingredients:
4 trout, cleaned and gutted.
Marinade ingredients:
50g/2oz any kind of sugar; 2 tbsp sake; 2 tbsp sweet sherry; 4 tbsp hoisin or plum sauce; 2 tbsp pineapple or orange juice; 125g/4oz miso paste (optional).

METHOD:
Mix up the marinade thoroughly. Put the trout in a wide, shallow dish and make several diagonal slashes in the skin down both sides to allow the marinade to seep in. Coat the trout thoroughly in the marinade on both sides. Cover and refrigerate for 4 or 5 hours, turning occasionally to give the marinade a chance to work its way in. When ready to eat, put the grill on high, place the fish on the grill rack and grill until done (eyes turn opaque), turning frequently and basting with marinade.

Serves 4.

Sake Salmon

Though rather expensive, this dish is so good that I think it is worth pushing the boat out once in a while. Not only does it taste delicious, but it is so true to the spirit of Japanese cooking and has all the virtues of being light, healthy, slimming and delicate, yet very satisfying.

Ingredients:
500g/1lb fresh salmon, thinly sliced and cut into strips; 1 piece crystallised stem ginger, finely chopped; 1 garlic clove, crushed; 2 spring
onions, chopped; 1 tsp any kind of sugar; 1 tsp salt; 50ml/2 fl oz soy
sauce; 50ml/2 fl oz sake; 50ml/2 fl oz sweet sherry.

METHOD:
Put the salmon strips in a large shallow dish. Mix up all the other ingredients very thoroughly, making sure all the sugar has dissolved. Pour
the marinade over the salmon, stir and cover. Leave to marinate thoroughly in the fridge for 1 hour. Remove the fish from the marinade. If
you have plenty of marinade left over, put it into a saucepan and bring
to a fierce simmer. When it has reduced to a thin gravy consistency,
cool it and serve as a dipping sauce. If possible serve the salmon on
a flat Japanese serving dish. Very often a shallow black glass dish is
used to show off the deep colour acquired by the salmon – most
people will think it's the finest rare roast beef until they taste it.
  Serves 2–4 (depending on greed).

Wine Stew

Another special favourite, the version of this recipe I am giving uses
herrings as the main ingredient. Certainly most Japanese would
choose herrings for preference, as herring is a very popular fish in
Japanese cuisine. From a health point of view this is a good option
because it is high in fish oils which are thought to protect against
heart disease. Ironically in Britain, which is surrounded by some of
the world's best herring fishing, herring is not a highly regarded fish.
If you condemn the herring you can substitute fresh large sardines,
mackerel or mullet, but I do urge you to give the humble herring a
fair trial.

Ingredients:
4 large herrings, cleaned, gutted and filleted.
Marinade ingredients:

8 tbsp sake or any kind of sherry; 50ml/2 fl oz white wine; 50ml/2 fl oz soy sauce; 2 tbsp any kind of sugar.
For garnish:
I tbsp chopped parsley; I tbsp chopped chives; I tsp black pepper.

METHOD:
Rinse and wipe the herrings and cut each one in two lengthways. Make three cuts in the skin side of each fish and put in a large shallow dish. Combine all the baste ingredients and use a brush or spoon to baste the fish liberally. Arrange the fish on a rack under the grill, skin side towards the heat, and grill for 5 minutes. Transfer the fish to a hobproof dish – preferably something nice enough to serve straight from – and pour over the remainder of the wine marinade. Put on the hob and simmer gently until the fish is lightly cooked through (no more than a few minutes), then serve in its sauce. A nice touch for a party is to flame the dish as you serve it. To do this remove about 2 tbsp of the sauce and combine it with a little hot brandy in a pan. Set light to this and pour it over the fish. Garnish with the parsley, chives and pepper.
    Serves 4.

Salty Fish

Many Japanese dishes feature fish that is by our standards very heavily salted. Some researchers believe that this may be a contributing factor in the high Japanese rates of stomach cancer. For this reason I have not included any of these dishes – many of us would find them too salty anyway. However, there is one version which is both very simple and allows for excess salt to be wiped off. Instead of suggesting it as a main course I am including it here to be used as a side dish along with rice and vegetables.

Ingredients:
I herring or mackerel, cleaned and gutted; I tbsp salt.

METHOD:
Wash the fish and dry. Rub all over with the salt and leave for about 30 minutes in the fridge. Before cooking wipe off excess salt and liquid. Grill under a medium heat for 10–15 minutes until thoroughly cooked. Remove from grill, take off the bone and chop into small pieces. Sprinkle on boiled rice.

Serves 4 as a garnish.

Chestnut Rice

This is a very seasonal dish both in Japan and in Britain. The fresh chestnut season in this country is in November and December, and although tinned chestnuts are available all year round I think it is nicer to save the dish for the autumn and the fresh chestnuts. Today seasonal ingredients in cooking are so easily disregarded that many dishes have lost that specialness of only being possible at certain times of the year.

Ingredients:
450g/1lb raw short grain rice; approx. 500g/just over 1lb fresh chestnuts (weighed in the shell); 2 tbsp sake or any kind of sherry; 1 tsp salt.

METHOD:
Soak rice for 1 hour, which helps to make the short grain rice particularly absorbent for this recipe. Meanwhile cook and peel the chestnuts. You can either do this by parboiling and peeling them, or by roasting and opening. Neither method is quick or easy. The alternative is to buy a medium-size tin of ready-prepared chestnuts. Drain the rice and put it in a pan with enough water to cover. When the rice is nearly completely cooked and fluffy, drain off any remaining water and stir in the sake, salt and chestnuts. Allow to cook on for 1–2 minutes while stirring until the sake is completely absorbed. Serve.

Serves 4–6.

Japanese Risotto

Known in Japanese as "maze gohan", this is one of those simple dishes, using up the leftovers, which rapidly finds its way into any household's weekly menu. The ingredients I have given are by no means written in stone; as you get used to this cooking style you will rapidly get the idea of using more or less anything that comes to hand.

Ingredients:
700g/1½lb raw short grain rice (pre-soaked as in previous recipe); 2 dried mushrooms, soaked until rehydrated and chopped; 1 sugar-lump size piece of fresh root ginger, peeled and chopped; 2 tbsp soy sauce; 1 tbsp sake; 2 carrots (raw or cooked, sliced); 2 celery stalks, chopped; 125g/4oz green peas (raw or cooked); 125g/4oz shrimps, shelled (frozen or tinned if desired).

METHOD:
Put the rice, mushrooms, ginger, soy sauce and sake into a heavy saucepan and cover with water. Bring to the boil and then simmer gently for about 15 minutes, stirring occasionally. When nearly all liquid is absorbed, add the rest of the ingredients and simmer for a further 5 minutes (longer if using raw ingredients). Stir occasionally and add a little more water if necessary. Once everything is thoroughly cooked and all the liquid absorbed, turn into a large bowl and serve.

Serves 4.

Shiitake Noodles

Not only is this dish simple and filling, but men will be interested to discover that the shiitake mushrooms which are a major ingredient are thought to be protective against heart disease.

Ingredients:

1 packet dried noodles; 1 tbsp sesame oil; 450g/1lb fresh shiitake mushrooms, sliced; 2 tbsp hoisin or plum sauce; 1 tbsp soy sauce; ½ pint (10 fl oz/300ml) dashi stock; 1 tbsp sake.

METHOD:

Put the noodles in water to cook, which will take about 10 minutes. While they are cooking, heat the oil in a deep frying pan and stir-fry the mushrooms. When they have absorbed all the oil and are browning nicely, add the hoisin or plum sauce, the soy sauce and the dashi stock. Keep simmering gently until the liquid is beginning to be thick and gravy-like. Add the sake. The noodles should be ready by now, so drain these into a large serving dish, stir in the shiitake mushroom sauce and serve.

Serves 2–4.

Seaweed Rice

This is a very simple, basic dish which can either be an accompaniment to a main course, or a main course in itself if you want to be especially frugal – if you are slimming or going through a phase of ultra-healthy eating.

Ingredients:

250g/8oz raw short grain rice; ½ cup white wine vinegar; 2 tbsp any kind of sugar; 1 tsp salt; 6 strips nori.

METHOD:

Cook the rice, drain off any excess liquid and stir in the vinegar, sugar and salt. Put to one side. If desired, crisp up the nori strips by grilling one side. In a serving dish put alternate layers of nori and rice until all the ingredients are used up. Reheat in the oven and serve.

Serves 2.

Sunday Rice

Nearly all the rice dishes described in this book use only boiled rice – a far more healthy and slimming option than fried rice. In fact boiled rice is by far the most common form of rice eaten in the Far East. Fried rice is eaten as a snack meal or junk food, rather in the way we would eat a burger when we're in a hurry, but never include it in a dinner party. However, we can't all be totally authentic the whole time, and if ever there was a day for indulging yourself, Sunday is it – so this recipe sees the rice getting a jolly good frying. Leftover rice is recommended because it is drier and fries up really well.

Ingredients:
2 tbsp sesame oil; 110g/4oz cubes ham, cooked pork or bacon bits; 50g/2oz peas, cooked; 2 oranges, segmented; 1 small tin pineapple chunks; 2 tbsp soy sauce; 450g/1lb rice, cooked, cold, preferably leftover.

METHOD:
Heat 1 tbsp of the oil in a frying pan and fry the ham and peas. Add the oranges and the drained pineapple chunks, reserving the juice. Keep stirring so it doesn't stick. Add the soy sauce and the juice from the pineapple chunks. Take off the heat while you see to the rice. In another deep frying pan heat the remaining oil and put in the rice. Dry fry the rice until it is very hot – it may even start to puff up like rice crispies at this stage, but don't worry about this. Keep stirring rice to make sure it doesn't stick or burn. When it is hot and puffy, transfer it to an ovenproof serving dish to keep warm in the oven. Now reheat the sweet ham sauce mixture, stirring continuously, until it is bubbling fiercely and beginning to caramelise. Take off the heat, remove the rice from the oven, pour on the sweet ham sauce. There should be quite a sizzling display as the hot sauce meets the rice and the resulting combination will have a wonderful taste and texture, as well as colour.
  Serves 4 depending on appetite.

Singapore Noodles

This is another rather "junky" recipe in Japanese eyes, and therefore doesn't require truly authentic Ingredients. For example, when I make this I use the packets of dried noodles that you see next to the dried pasta and spaghetti on supermarket shelves. You can use fresh noodles if they are available at your local deli counter, but I don't think it makes much difference. To the Japanese this is very much a convenience food and a comfort food – and a way of using up leftovers – so it's important to keep it simple.

Ingredients:
1 pint (10 fl oz/600ml) stock; 1 packet dried noodles; 1 egg; 10g/3-½ oz prawns (frozen, fresh or tinned); 1 cup peas, cooked; 4 slices cooked meat (leftovers, ham, whatever), chopped; 1 tsp five spice powder; 1 tbsp any kind of sherry or sake; 1 tbsp soy sauce.

METHOD:
Bring stock to boil. Put in packet of dried noodles. Leave to simmer gently. Meanwhile break the egg into a large soup tureen or similar. When the noodles have absorbed about half the water, chuck in the rest of the ingredients and leave to simmer briefly until the noodles are quite soft. Pour the pan contents straight onto the egg, stirring as you pour. The egg will be partially set and give a delicious extra something. Serve immediately.

Serves 2–4. depending on appetite

Geisha Grill

This is so delicious that I've called it Geisha Grill because my husband says it's the only time I really look after him.

Ingredients:
450g/1lb chicken breasts; 125g/4oz chicken livers; 12 small onions, halved; 3 tbsp light soy sauce; 3 tbsp any kind of sherry or sake; 1½ tbsp any kind of sugar; black pepper.

METHOD:
Cube the chicken and livers and thread onto skewers alternating with onions. Put the soy sauce, sherry and sugar in a pan. Mix and heat until just simmering. Meanwhile grill the chicken skewers under a hot grill basting every so often with the hot mixture. Keep turning and basting until the meat is well done with a high glaze. Serve on a bed of plain boiled rice sprinkled with black pepper and soy sauce.

Serves 2 as a main course, 4 as a starter.

Pickles Rice Pick

Winters can be extremely hard in parts of Japan and lots of pickled vegetables are a fail-safe stand-by in the kitchen during those months. Perhaps because of their associations with cosying up for the winter, they are also seen as something of a comfort food by the Japanese. Making your own Japanese pickles can be rather time-consuming, but fortunately they and the very similar Chinese versions are now widely available in supermarkets, delicatessens and Oriental stores. The pickled cabbage is my favourite, so the recipe here includes it along with another refreshing pickle that is easy to make yourself.

Ingredients:
1 medium-size jar of pickled cabbage; ½ cucumber, peeled and thinly sliced; 1 onion, sliced thinly into rings; 4 tbsp red wine vinegar; 2 tbsp malt vinegar; black pepper; 450g/1lb raw short grain rice; 2 tbsp white wine vinegar; 1 tbsp sake.

METHOD:
Turn out the jar of pickled cabbage onto a serving dish; that is pickle number one. Next arrange the cucumber and onion in a wide, shallow dish. Cover liberally with the red wine and malt vinegars. Sprinkle with black pepper and leave it to soak; that is pickle number two. Now prepare your rice by boiling in the usual way. When it is fluffy drain it into a serving dish and sprinkle on the white wine

vinegar and sake. Serve together with the two pickles. The contrast between the blandness of the rice and the sharpness of the vinegar is excellent.

Serves 2–4 depending on whether serving as a main or a side dish.

Teppan Bean Curd

Teppan is one of those dishes that pops up so frequently in Oriental cookery that it is hard to work out where it originated. However, I suspect that the name teppan is a corruption of the Chinese "tai pan", which would translate into "merchant prince" in English. The dish didn't become well known in Japan until after the Second World War. Teppan is cooked on a special cast iron griddle called a teppan which can be bought from Oriental stores as well as specialist kitchen shops. The griddle comes with a special wooden base so that it can be moved straight from the hob to the table. A good heavy frying pan can be substituted. Detailed instructions on equipment for teppan are given on page 86.

Ingredients:
1 tsp soya oil; 1 small onion, sliced; 2 sticks celery, thinly sliced; 2 tomatoes, sliced; 1 pack bean curd, drained and thickly sliced; 2 tbsp orange juice; 1 tbsp soy sauce; 1 tsp any kind of sugar; 1 tsp sake.

METHOD:
Heat your griddle or pan until very hot and pour in the oil. Add the onion and celery, followed by the tomatoes and bean curd. Don't stir, it doesn't matter if the bottom sticks, or even begins to burn. Turn the bean curd over a couple of times. Mix together the orange juice, soy sauce, sugar and sake. When everything is very hot, just before serving pour on the orange juice mixture and allow it all to sizzle and spit. The idea is that the sauce should caramelise into the other ingredients. Serve and eat while it is all sizzling.

Serves 2.

Chicken Teriyaki

Even the most unadventurous gourmet will fall for this dish, it is so easy to enjoy and international in its appeal. It is probably the dish most frequently ordered in Japanese restaurants outside Japan.

Ingredients:
125ml/4 fl oz soy sauce; 1 inch/2.5cm piece fresh root ginger, peeled and chopped; 1 clove garlic, crushed; 125ml/4 fl oz dry white wine; 2 tbsp clear honey; 6 chicken breasts, skinned and boned.

METHOD:
Make a marinade of the soy sauce, ginger, garlic and white wine and put to one side. Heat the honey in a small saucepan until it is runny. Arrange the chicken breasts on a large shallow dish and brush them thoroughly on both sides with honey, then pour on the marinade and leave to steep for 2 hours at room temperature. Preheat a moderate oven (180°C, Gas Mark 4, 350°F). Remove the breasts from the marinade and put into a baking tin. Bake in the oven, basting frequently with remaining marinade, for 30–35 minutes until the chicken is cooked through and tender. Place on serving dish and pour cooking juices over the top.
   Serves 6.

Yaki Tori Chicken

A great many Japanese restaurants specialise solely in table-top cooking, and yaki tori is one of their typical dishes. If you ever get a chance to go to a Japanese table-top cooking restaurant (see the list on pages 187–9), do try it. Even though it can be expensive, it is great fun.

Ingredients:
450g/1lb chicken breasts, skinned, boned and cut into bite-size pieces; 450g/1lb leeks, blanched and cut into ½ inch/1cm sections; 175ml/6 fl oz soy sauce; 175ml/6 fl oz sweet sherry.

METHOD:
Thread the chicken pieces onto small bamboo or wooden skewers (from Oriental stores and cook shops, also available in supermarkets). It is a good idea to wrap the exposed ends of the skewers with foil (dull side out) to prevent scorching, or soak them in water before threading. Separately thread the leeks onto skewers. Next make the sauce by simmering the soy sauce and the sherry together in a pan until it begins to thicken. Remove from heat. Put the skewers of chicken and leek under a hot grill, with the leeks furthest from the heat. Cook for 3 minutes. Take off the chicken and leek skewers and dip them in the sauce until thoroughly coated. Put them back under the grill for another 2–3 minutes and then coat them in another layer of sauce. Repeat this process until the chicken is completely cooked. Serve straight away, with any remaining sauce as a dip.

Serves 4.

Asian Rolls

I've called these Asian Rolls because they are the sort of dish you will find all over Asia, rather than specifically in Japan. I think they are probably Vietnamese somewhere along the line, but really they are just a typical snack of the Pacific Rim.

Ingredients:
1 tbsp sesame oil; ½ tsp mixed spice or five spice powder; 1 onion, diced; 2 pieces crystallised stem ginger, diced; 2 cloves garlic, crushed; 340g/12 oz minced meat (preferably pork); 2 or 3 tbsp hoisin or plum sauce; 1 tbsp soy sauce; 8–10 large crisp lettuce leaves; 4 spring onions, in slivers.

METHOD:
In a deep frying pan heat the oil and add the spice powder, onion, ginger and garlic, frying until soft. Add the minced meat and the sauces, and continue to stir-fry. Cover the pan and simmer for about

15 minutes, stirring regularly. You may need to add a little stock or water to prevent it sticking, but keep the mixture as dry as possible. While the meat is cooking, arrange the lettuce leaves and spring onions on separate dishes. When the meat is really tender and all the sauce is absorbed, turn it into a serving dish. The way to eat this is to take a lettuce leaf and spread it with the mince, together with a sprinkling of spring onion slivers. Then roll the whole thing up into a cigar and eat with the fingers. You can serve a dipping sauce (teriyaki sauce is best) to dip the rolls into if you like.

Serves 2–4.

Simple Stir-Fry

When you're used to the Japanese Diet this is the sort of dish you'll throw together without even thinking. You'll substitute different ingredients so often that your version will become completely unrecognisable from mine. Here's a basic starter kit.

Ingredients:

1 or 2 tsp soya oil; 6 celery stalks, chopped; 1 cup French beans, whole; 2 cloves garlic, sliced; 4 large green or red peppers (capsicums), sliced; ½ head Chinese leaves, sliced into ribbons; pinch five spice powder; Japanese soy sauce to taste; ½ cup stock; small bunch fresh coriander or flat-leaf parsley, roughly chopped; 1 pack bean curd, drained, sliced or chopped thickly.

METHOD:

Heat the oil in a deep non-stick frying pan. Add celery, French beans and garlic and stir-fry until they begin to soften. Add peppers and continue stir-frying briefly (under a minute). Add Chinese leaves. Sprinkle on five spice powder, Japanese soy sauce and soy sauce to taste. Pour on the stock. When stock starts to simmer, carefully add the coriander and the soya bean curd. Turn the bean curd a few times until it is hot, but be gentle, otherwise you will break it up into crumbs. Serve straight onto individual plates.

Serves 2 as a main course.

SPECIAL MEALS

Simple Sushi

Ingredients for the rice:
4 cups short grain rice; 4½ cups water; 1 cup white malt vinegar; ½ tbsp salt, ½ tbsp sugar.

METHOD (MAKES APPROX 10–20 SUSHI):
At breakfast time put the rice to soak in cold water. At lunch time it will be ready for you to drain. Boil up the water and add the rice, cover and leave to simmer until all the water has been absorbed. Put the rice in a bowl and pour in the vinegar mixed with the salt and the sugar, stirring so it is all absorbed. Leave to one side or cover and put in the fridge for later. (Do not leave cold rice sitting in the fridge for more than a couple of days as it will gradually become less fresh; always cover to prevent tainting).

Ingredients for toppings:
Small pack sliced smoked salmon; small jar mock caviar; jar cockles in vinegar; any leftovers (cold peas, etc.); large flat spinach leaves; soy sauce; minced onion; grated ginger or horseradish.

METHOD:
With wet hands take a lump of rice slightly smaller than a golfball and roll into a ball. Make about 6 balls. Now take one spinach leaf and lay it flat on a chopping board with one slice of smoked salmon on top. Take one of your rice balls and roll it in your hand until it is a fat sausage. Put the rice sausage on the spinach and salmon, and wrap it up as though wrapping a bottle. Trim the ends and chop into

sections 1 inch/2.5cm wide. Place the section flat on your serving dish. Congratulations, you just made your first sushi snack.

The next one is going to be a different shape. Take another rice ball and flatten it slightly. Press your thumb into the middle to leave a very slight dent. Spoon 1 tsp of mock caviar onto the rice and put a couple of cockles on top. Place on the serving dish.

Here's another shape. Take your ball of rice and sprinkle some soy sauce over it, rolling the ball round until the sprinkle has spread over the surface. Now roll it in the minced onion so that the pieces cling to it and then do the same with the grated ginger. Place on the serving dish.

As you get used to the methods and the way you can work the rice, you will get creative, so basically it is up to you to go on until you want to stop. When you have completed the dish to your satisfaction, sprinkle with sushi with grated horseradish or ginger and add any extra garnish you want.

When you get more used to the tastes of Japanese food, you can become more authentic and use the strips of nori seaweed and the marinated fish which would be part of the real thing. Or if you never get to that point, don't worry – but remember you'll be missing out on all those healthy benefits, and as we tell our children, "You'll never know whether you like it if you don't try it." for the brave, here are a couple of more authentic Japanese sushi snacks.

With Seaweed

Ingredients:
1 cup short grain rice, boiled; rice sauce to taste (see below); 2 sheets nori, shredded.

METHOD:
Press the rice into flat squares (you can buy frames for making the squares in Oriental stores, otherwise use a couple of knives dipped in hot water). Sandwich the rice between two layers of nori and trim the edges. You have the authentic Japanese sandwich!

With Marinated Fish (Real Nigiri Sushi)

Ingredients:
1 mackerel fillet; marinade (see below); 1 cup short grain rice, boiled; rice sauce to taste (see below); 2 sheets nori, shredded; 1 cup green beans, chopped.
Marinade ingredients:
1 tsp salt; 1 tsp lemon juice; 2 tbsp wine vinegar; 1 tbsp Soy sauce.
Rice sauce ingredients:
1 tsp horseradish sauce, mixed to a thin dip with equal parts soy sauce and wine vinegar.

METHOD:
First blanch your mackerel by pouring boiling water over it, followed immediately by very cold water. Pat dry with a paper towel. Skin the mackerel and slice in thin strips, placing them on a shallow dish. Mix up the marinade and coat the mackerel thoroughly, turning the pieces over so the marinade is evenly spread. Leave covered in the fridge for 15 minutes. Press the rice into small flattened balls and garnish with layers of fish, nori and green beans. Serve with rice sauce for dipping into.

Sashimi

Version One: Marinade

Ingredients:
Good quality fish, (salmon, sole, tuna, mackerel) very fresh, filleted. Marinade of 2 tsp horseradish sauce; 2 tbsp lemon juice; 2 tbsp soy sauce; 1 tsp any kind of vinegar.

METHOD:
Rinse the fish first in boiling water and then iced water. Cut the fillets crossways against the grain into very thin strips. Make up the

marinade and place the strips in it. Leave covered in the fridge for about 20 minutes. Remove from marinade, arrange on a dish with a coriander leaf garnish and serve with a little soy sauce, teriyaki sauce or horseradish as a dip.

Version Two: Salted

Ingredients:
Good quality, firm, sweet-fleshed fish (salmon, sole, tuna – mackerel is a little too strong flavoured for this method), very fresh, filleted; salt.

METHOD:
Wash the fish fillets and sprinkle them with salt. Cover and leave in the fridge for 20–30 minutes. Cut fish across the grain into bite-size pieces. Serve with a dip.

Sukiyaki

Sukiyaki is one of Japan's cordon bleu meals, and it is the sort of dish you will come across if you eat out at Japanese restaurants. It is also my personal all-time favourite Japanese dish and sukiyaki is one dish I think the whole family will enjoy. There is plenty of tender lean beefsteak to keep traditionalists happy and the cooking method is such fun that children will enjoy it too. In fact sukiyaki is one of the most Western influenced of all Japanese dishes, because meat was not originally part of the Japanese diet. In the last century the increasing opening of Japan to Western trade and influence brought meat into the diet and resulted in the wonderful marriage of an essentially Western ingredient with a typically Japanese cooking technique. You can cook this meal at the table or in the kitchen. For table cooking you will need some special cooking utensils, but anyone who fell for the 1970s fondue craze will be delighted to find a use for the fondue kit at last.

The quantities I have given are on an individual basis for the meat and egg because these are the two important things (particularly from a slimmer's point of view), but the amounts of other ingredients would comfortably serve around 4 to 6 – since they are cheap and nutritious I wouldn't bother making big adjustments in them for the number of people being served. Again experience will help you calculate how much of which ingredient you and your family like. A full description of table-top cooking and its equipment is given on pages 84–5.

Ingredients:

125g/4oz per person good steak (fillet is best), cut across the grain into thin strips; 250g/8oz small fresh spinach leaves; 250g/8oz small mushrooms, stalks removed and caps halved; 2 carrots, cut into strips; 250g/8oz cold, part-boiled ordinary or cellophane noodles; 12 spring onions, sliced; 1 pack bean curd, drained and cubed; 250ml/ 8 fl oz dashi stock (or substitute – see Cooking Methods section); 125 ml/ 4 fl oz soya sauce; 2 tbsp soft brown sugar. 125 ml/4 fl oz sake or dry sherry; 1 egg per person.

METHOD:

On your favourite serving dish arrange the steak pieces, spinach leaves, mushrooms, carrots, spring onions and bean curd. Put in the centre of the table or by the cookery commander's place! Now make the cooking stock by mixing the dashi stock, soy sauce, sugar and sake together. Pour into a large jug. Break each egg into a small individual bowl and beat lightly. Put a large, heavy flameproof pot (a fondue dish is ideal) over a low heat and grease the inside with a little fat. If you are cooking sukiyaki as a table top meal this is the point where everybody selects one or two favourite bits to start with (most people go for the steak first!) and puts them into the pot. Now pour on enough of the cooking stock to give a good covering to the ingredients everybody has put in and simmer for about 5 minutes, with everybody having the chance to stir the stock and keep an eye on their personal ingredients. When the steak has cooked through and any vegetables are beginning to be tender (not soft) it is time to remove them. At a communal cook-in it is customary for people to pick out their own with chopsticks, otherwise you can lift them out with a slotted spoon.

This stage is where the egg per person comes in. Each diner pours a little of their beaten egg into the bottom of their bowl before adding a selection of the hot, cooked steak, curd and vegetables and ladling on a little of the cooking stock. A quick stir coats all the cooked items with the egg which rapidly cooks into and thickens the cooking stock into a delicious sauce coating the food. The whole thing makes a flavour that really is unique, as well as a lovely texture and feel in the mouth.

Now comes the best part, you all do it all over again! Each time you have another round of cooking add some more stock and so on until everybody is full or most of the ingredients are used up. Towards the end you may find the stock becomes too concentrated or the ingredients may start sticking to the bottom of the pan, in which case turn the heat down and add a little water. Experience will tell you how to keep it all in the right proportion. If you are cooking this dish on the hob in the kitchen, I recommend you cook all the ingredients at once in one large casserole and then place the dish on a plate warmer on the table to keep it hot while everyone helps themselves. However it has to be admitted that the meal does lose a little something if not cooked at the table.

Serves 4–6.

Here's a quick step-by-step guide to preparing Sukiyaki:

1. Get all your ingredients together – 125g/4oz steak per person; bean curd cut into 1inch/2.5cm cubes; part-cooked cold noodles; button mushrooms, stalks removed; tin of sliced bamboo shoots, drained; small fresh spinach leaves; thin slices of carrot; slivers of spring onion.
2. Arrange the ingredients attractively on serving dishes on the table.
3. Lay the table with chopsticks or forks and bowls or plates for each diner. Put a small bowl of beaten raw egg alongside each place.

4. Make a stock in the following proportions: 2 parts sake or dry sherry; 3 parts soy sauce; 4 parts dashi stock. Add brown sugar to taste.
5. Heat a heavy oiled casserole over a low heat until hot and pour in the stock to about one inch deep. Keep back the rest of the stock for topping up the pan as it boils away during cooking.
6. When the stock is bubbling take it to the table where it will be kept hot over a burner or table-top cooker.
7. The meal commences, with everyone selecting their ingredients, placing them in the stock and leaving until cooked (about 4 minutes depending on taste and ingredient).
8. Before eating the ingredient is dipped in the egg which cooks as it coats the hot ingredient.

Teriyaki

When you have chosen your meat and decided how much you will serve (probably 125–200g/4–7oz per person), cut it into small-ish slices and leave it to marinate for about 2 hours in one of the marinades described below. Version one is best if you are going to grill, and version two is better for frying.

When you have marinated the meat, cook it lightly under the grill or in a pan with a little hot oil – no more than 2 or 3 minutes per side. While cooking, brush frequently with the remains of the marinade. Serve with boiled rice and salad, or if you are eating with the family it goes equally well with baked potatoes or chips and vegetables.

Marinade – Version One:
1 inch/2.5 cm piece fresh root ginger, peeled and finely chopped; 2 cloves garlic crushed; 25g/1oz brown sugar; 250ml/8 fl oz soy sauce; 125ml/4 fl oz sake; salt and pepper.

Marinade – Version Two:
50ml/2 fl oz dry sherry; 2 tbsp soy sauce; 1 clove garlic, crushed; 50ml/2 fl oz dashi stock; 1 tbsp plum or hoisin sauce.

Tempura

The major part of a tempura meal is usually prawns, along with a range of fish, seafood and salad vegetables. Each uncooked ingredient is individually dipped in a delicious light coating of batter and then deep-fried at the table.

Here is a step-by-step guide to doing your own tempura. Remember you will need a table-top cooking set.

1. First get your ingredients together. Judge quantities by how much you think people will eat and select your choice from the following: fresh prawns (preferably uncooked); scallops; fish; mussels; squid; button mushrooms; sugar snap (mangetout) peas; green peppers (capsicums); cauliflower florets; broccoli; carrots; bamboo shoots; green beans; spinach leaves.
2. Lay out all the ingredients in bite size pieces on serving dishes and place on the table.
3. Lay the table with chopsticks or fondue forks and bowls or plates and a small bowl of soy or teriyaki sauce per person.
4. Prepare the batter, blending together 1 egg, 1 egg yolk, 175ml/6 fl oz water, 125g/4oz flour (this gives enough coating batter for 6–8 people).
5. Give each person an individual bowl of batter (prevents mess – and fights!).
6. Light the table burner and heat a deep frying pan which is one third full of oil (a blend of about three quarters your normal oil and one quarter sesame oil works well).
7. When the oil is hot everyone can begin cooking and eating.
8. Keep an eye on the oil to make sure it doesn't become too hot. A good tip is floating a piece of bread in the cooking oil which slows it down and collects any excess batter.

9

FAST FOODS AND NIBBLES

JAPANESE FAST FOODS

SOYA BEAN CURD (TOFU)

It may sound very different from foods we are used to eating in the West, but in fact tofu or bean curd is just as simple to cook with as any of our basic ingredients – it would never have achieved such widespread popularity in China and Japan if it was difficult to cope with. It fulfils very much the same role in Oriental cuisine as cheese, cottage cheese and yogurt do in ours. It fits easily into any number of recipes, is quick to prepare and can be used cooked or plain in many different ways.

BEAN CURD SNACK RECIPES

Tofu (Bean Curd) Dip

Ingredients:

1 pack (285g/10oz) bean curd; salt and pepper to taste; 8 tbsp sour cream; 200g/7oz flaked tinned tuna *or* grated blue cheese *or* cooked spinach purée *or* finely chopped mushrooms.

METHOD:

Wrap bean curd in a teatowel and allow to drain for 15 minutes.

Place all the ingredients in the blender and whizz until you are satisfied with the texture. If the result is too runny for your preference, thicken with breadcrumbs. If it is too thick, thin it with olive oil, or if you are counting calories use the juice drained from the bean curd. The consistency of the dip will be different depending on which ingredient you are using. When you are accustomed to making tofu dips you can adjust seasonings and ingredients to your taste. Try seasoning with soy sauce, horseradish, garlic or mustard. Serve with raw vegetable sticks, toast, bread or crispbread.

Serves 4.

Quick Bean Curd Fry

Ingredients:
285g/10oz bean curd; salt and pepper to taste; flour; soya or sesame oil; garnish (to your choice).

METHOD:
Press the bean curd as described above. Cut into slices 1 × 2 inches (2.5cm × 5cm) and 1/4 inch (7mm) thick. Sprinkle with salt and pepper or any preferred seasoning. Dredge thoroughly with flour. Heat oil in a saucepan and fry bean curd slices carefully, turning regularly, until they are crisp and golden. Arrange slices on a plate and garnish with anything you have to hand (tomato slices, anchovies, shrimps, chopped chives, etc).

Serves 2.

Bean Curd Spread

Ingredients:
285g/10oz bean curd, drained; 180g/6oz smoked fish fillet (trout, salmon, mackerel, haddock, etc); 3 tbsp olive oil; 3 tbsp any kind of vinegar; 1 tsp any kind of mustard; seasoning to taste.

METHOD:
Crumble curd into a saucepan and cook over a high heat for 2 minutes, stirring continuously. Squeeze in a cloth to get rid of moisture. Put with all the other ingredients in a blender and whizz until you have a pâté-like spread. Serve on toast garnished with capers or minced onion.

Serves 2–4.

Bean Curd Cream Soup

Ingredients:
500g/1lb 2oz marrow; 285g/10oz bean curd, drained; 250ml/9 fl oz litre milk; 1 stock cube; 2 tbsp cornflour; salt to taste; chopped chives.

METHOD:
Peel, deseed and chop the marrow. Simmer gently in a little water until completely soft and pulpy. Add water as necessary to prevent burning. Allow to cool and blend in the blender with the bean curd until smooth. Bring milk to a simmer in a pan, stir in stock cube and marrow/bean curd mixture. Allow to simmer gently for about 10 minutes. Blend cornflour with a little water and stir into soup to thicken it. When soup has thickened, allow to simmer for another moment or two before serving with chives. Almost any vegetable can be substituted for marrow, especially leftover peas, beans or potatoes.

Serves 2–4 as main course or starter

NOODLES
Basically for noodles, think chips! Though they are nutritionally superior (lower in fat, higher in trace elements, etc) noodles, like chips, are a carbohydrate staple food, easy to prepare and eaten frequently as part of fast-food meals. Unlike chips, noodles can be eaten hot or cold, so perhaps potatoes in general would be a fairer comparison. To cook them, follow the directions on the packet or specific recipe. Mainly this will just be a matter of chucking them in boiling water or stock until they are cooked.

Dressed Noodles

Ingredients:

1 packet dried long egg noodles (not the tight packed, curly ones); 2 tbsp oyster sauce; 1 tbsp sesame oil; 1 tsp sesame seeds; optional garnish of chopped chives, parsley, etc.

METHOD:

Simmer the noodles in water till cooked. Drain and serve into a large bowl. Add oyster sauce and oil, and using salad servers toss thoroughly until the sauce and oil are evenly distributed. Sprinkle with sesame seeds and garnish. Serve as an accompaniment or on its own as a warming, quick snack meal.

Serves 2 as a snack lunch.

Noodle Soup

Ingredients:

1 small packet dried curly noodles; 1 pint (20 fl oz/600ml) stock; ½ bunch watercress, roughly chopped; 2 inches/5cm cucumber, cut into matchsticks.

METHOD:

Cook the noodles in the stock. When the noodles are nearly done add the watercress and simmer briefly (1 minute). Just before serving, stir in the cucumber strips and allow them to become transparent.

Serves 2.

Fried Noodles

Ingredients:

1 tbsp olive oil; 2 cloves garlic, finely chopped; 1 inch/2.5cm piece fresh root ginger, peeled and finely chopped; 1 onion, sliced; 1 packet noodles, cooked; 2–4oz/50–100g chopped ham; 2 tbsp sweet and sour sauce.

METHOD:
Heat the oil and fry the garlic, ginger and onion until the onion is transparent. Add the noodles and keep frying until the noodles start to get crispy. Add the ham and turn over a few times before pouring on the sauce. Stir in the sauce, mix thoroughly and serve.
  Serves 2.

STIR-FRY SNACK RECIPES

Basic stir frying techniques have already been described in the cooking methods section, here are a few recipes to get you started for quick lunches and suppers. One of the most popular ways of cooking bean curd is by stir-frying. If you are going to cook your bean curd like this, try to choose a firm variety (check the pack) or you can poach your block of curd quickly and gently in boiling water to firm it up. Then slice it and coat the slices in flour before frying quickly on both sides in sesame oil. Turn the slices gently in order not to break up the curd and let it turn a lovely golden colour with a slight crispy coat – delicious.

Light Fry

Ingredients:
1 tbsp sesame oil; 1 inch/2.5cm piece fresh root ginger, peeled and chopped; 2 cloves garlic, chopped; 1 onion, sliced; 1 small can water chestnuts; 1 tbsp soy sauce; 2 tsp sake or any kind of sherry; ½ cucumber, cut into matchsticks.

METHOD:
Heat the oil and add ginger and garlic. Fry briefly. Add onion and stir-fry until golden. Add water chestnuts and continue stir-frying while adding soy sauce and sherry. Allow all to sizzle briefly. Add

cucumber and stir-fry briefly until cucumber is transparent. Serve either as a lunch time snack on its own or with dressed noodles or as a vegetable accompaniment for a main meal.

Serves 1, or 2 as side dish.

Vegetable Fry

Ingredients:

2 tbsp olive oil; 4 cloves garlic, minced; 2 carrots, sliced diagonally in thin slivers; 4 sticks celery, sliced; 1/2 can (225g/7 oz) beansprouts drained; 1 avocado, sliced; 1 tbsp hoisin sauce; 1 tbsp any kind of sherry.

METHOD:

Heat the oil and stir-fry in this order: garlic, carrots, celery, bean sprouts. Stir in hoisin sauce and sherry. Lastly add the avocado which is very delicate and will need to be turned over in the mixture rather than stirred. When the avocado is thoroughly amalgamated, serve with rice.

Serves 2.

English-style Fry

Ingredients:

1 tbsp butter or fat; 4 rashers bacon, cut into pieces across the grain; 1 onion, finely sliced; 2 medium-size boiled potatoes, sliced; 1 tsp Worcestershire sauce.

METHOD:

Melt the fat and add the bacon. When the bacon has begun to release its juices, add the onions and pototoes. Stir-fry all together until bacon is crispy and onions and potato are golden. Sprinkle with Worcestershire sauce and serve.

Serves 2.

JAPANESE NIBBLES

Rice Crackers Bought in packets along with the nuts and nibbles section in the supermarket, these make a nice change from potato crisps and an interesting garnish for Japanese salads.

Nori For a truly Japanese nibble, spread nori sheets on the grill rack and grill ever so quickly on one side only. Don't let them burn. Eat sprinkled with soy sauce.

Mushrooms Raw mushrooms sprinkled with soy sauce are delicious, but some people don't like eating raw mushrooms, so just fry them quickly in soy sauce without any added oil and allow to cool for eating as a nibble.

Whitebait Many people love whitebait, and the Japanese are especially fond of dried whitebait (available in Oriental stores).

In one pan mix 1/2 cup of soy sauce, 1/2 cup any kind of sugar and 1½ tbsp sweet sherry (the Japanese would use mirin) and allow to simmer gently. While it is coming to a simmer, pinch off the heads of 150g/5oz dried whitebait and dry-fry them in another pan over a low heat until they look crisp. Pour on the sauce and keep stirring until the sauce has reduced to the point where it is a glaze. Take off the heat, put in a bowl and allow to cool. Serve cold (or even chilled). The end result is delicious, like a sort of savoury toffee.

Seafood Like East-End Londoners, the Japanese are very keen on fresh seafood as a nibble. But I find their version rather easier to get on with than jellied eel and whelks! They like small cooked shrimps or green-lipped mussels on the half-shell or cockles or mussels, cooked and served cold with a dipping sauce made up of soy sauce, sake, vinegar (and anything else you fancy really). The seafood is easily available on supermarket fish counters or frozen or pickled and it makes a nibble that is not only delicious but low-calorie and nutritious.

10

SEASONAL MENUS AND
SPECIAL OCCASIONS

One of the great pleasures of being on the Japanese Diet is that, unlike ordinary slimming diets, it is derived from a genuine national cuisine and so it lays great stress on being fun to eat. Most ordinary slimming diets are designed only to be followed for a short period of time, so the fact that they are boring and depressing to eat is ignored. But the Japanese follow the Japanese Diet all year round! And that means it has to be fun, varied, interesting and full of celebration opportunities.

Any national cuisine, whether British, Mediterranean or Oriental, fulfils many different roles for the people who eat it. At certain times it has to provide really special celebration foods for high days, feast days, holidays and birthdays. It also needs to have good, cheering comfort foods for horrible winter days when food seems to be the only nice thing around.

Every nation looks to its food to be adaptable. It must provide comfort in times of crisis; it must please everyone at large family gatherings or it must be capable of disappearing into the background at times when we are too busy to cook. When the weather is hot and fine, dishes need to be light and cooling – and preferably simple to prepare so we can spend more time outdoors. In the winter most of us look to food to make up for the lack of sunshine, as well as performing its practical function of keeping us warm.

Because it is a genuine national cuisine, as opposed to an artificial slimming diet, the Japanese Diet provides all those extra qualities that we look for in our own national cuisine. Very few ordinary slimming diets are based on what real people really eat day in day out, and this makes them very hard to stick to (as many of us will have experienced). What do you do on an ordinary diet when it's New Year or a Bank Holiday or people are coming for dinner or the weather's foul and you need cheering up? I think most of us agree that those are the danger times for breaking your diet.

Of course the Japanese have no problem with this, because naturally the Japanese Diet is what they eat all year round. So there are all sorts of fun foods and celebration menus. In England we enjoy a traditional winter Sunday lunch of roast beef and Yorkshire pudding or we have fish and chips when we feel like a break from complicated cooking, and the Japanese are just the same. New Year is a particularly important time for them, and there are all sorts of special treats to eat then.

The different seasons are reflected in Japanese cooking just as much as in European cooking – perhaps even more so, since Japan tends to have quite an extreme climate, with hot, humid summers and cold, snowy winters.

One difference perhaps is the Japanese attitude to the changing seasons. They tend to celebrate the arrival of each new season equally – emphasising its virtues rather than grumbling about its drawbacks. In spring the arrival of the cherry blossom has its own festival of recognition. Most British people would understand that very well, and our Spring and Easter Bank Holidays have a similar feel.

But what about the coming of winter and the first frosts? In Britain we try to pretend it's not happening (and so we always get taken by surprise on the first icy mornings) but in Japan they create opportunities to appreciate the good points of winter. There is even a special festival in late autumn to admire the beauty of the full moon – especially prized if it is reflecting off frost or a snow-covered landscape.

The Japanese recognise that winter can be very beautiful, and their winter food reflects positive qualities by being comforting, warming and fun to eat. That's what seasonal and celebration cooking on the Japanese Diet is all about. I'm sure you won't be eating authentic Japanese permanently after you've finished the first four weeks of the Japanese Diet, but why not have a few days on the Japanese Diet at the beginning of each new season, just to set you up for the weeks to come? Or incorporate some of these menus into your daily cooking and entertaining just for fun.

SPRING TREATS

Just as in Britain, spring is a time of new growth in Japan, when young, tender vegetables and fruits make cooking particularly easy and delicious. If you need to lose weight, this is about the best time to do it. Spring vegetables are at their most nutritious and fun to eat and you don't need the warming, cheering qualities of the high-calorie comfort foods you have been eating during the winter.

New-season bamboo shoots are the seasonal delicacy in Japan. They are called "takenoko" and have a delightful fragrance and sweet taste – no wonder Giant Pandas are so keen on them! Unfortunately you can't really get fresh, new bamboo shoots in Britain; we are on the other side of the world after all. But you can buy tinned bamboo shoots. However, I would substitute fresh asparagus tips as being more in keeping with the spirit of Japanese cooking. The point is that asparagus is a British speciality uniquely available in the spring and is very much our equivalent of bamboo shoots in Japan.

Another Japanese spring favourite is exactly the same in England – and that is the first early strawberries, so treat yourself to some, and try the sweet and savoury duck and strawberry salad included here.

The Japanese are very fond of cherry blossom, which features not only in their art and poetry – but even in their cooking! Extract of cherry blossom is used to flavour special cakes eaten in the spring – watch out for them in Oriental stores.

Generally Japanese spring cooking reflects the lightness of the season, with lots of fish and shellfish eaten, and even a special kind of mild tea, called "shin cha".

Spring Recipes

Strawberry and Duck Salad

Ingredients:
2 fresh duck breasts with skin; 1 large punnet strawberries; 1 pack fresh watercress; 3 tbsp flavoured vinegar or wine vinegar; 1 tbsp fruit juice (pineapple or orange); 1 tsp soy sauce; 2 tsp sesame oil; 1 tsp sesame seeds.

METHOD:
Grill the duck breasts, turning frequently until they are cooked through and the skin crispy. Put to one side to cool. Slice the strawberries and put in a large salad bowl with the watercress. Cut the duck breasts across the grain of the meat into thin slices and arrange on top of the strawberries and watercress. Mix all the other ingredients except the sesame seeds into a dressing and pour over the salad. Sprinkle with sesame seeds.

Serves 2 as a main course, 4 as a side salad.

Asparagus with Crab

Ingredients:
1 tsp any kind of oil; 1 bundle fresh asparagus (preferably British); 1 tin of crab meat; stock; 2 tsp cornflour blended with 2 tbsp white wine and 2 tbsp water.

METHOD:
Heat the oil in a deep frying pan. Cut the woody ends off the

asparagus and put them into the hot oil, turning them over gently until they shine with the oil coating. Allow them to continue frying briefly but not to burn and then pour on enough stock to cover. Cover the pan and allow to simmer gently until the asparagus shoots are soft. Add the crab meat and stir in. Then thicken with the cornflour mixture and serve immediately.

Serves 2.

Bamboo Shoot Special

Ingredients:

2 tsp sesame oil; 4 cloves garlic, crushed; I large can bamboo shoots, drained; 1/2 cucumber, sliced; I pack bean curd, drained, sliced and sprinkled with flour.

METHOD:

Heat I tsp of the oil in a deep pan and start frying the garlic and the bamboo shoots. Add the cucumber slices and keep stir-frying as they wilt. Next add the bean curd slices, turning carefully until the flour has incorporated into the liquid from the cucumber and bamboo. Turn into a dish and sprinkle with the remaining oil before serving.

Serves 2 as a side dish.

Sweet and Sour Spring Soup

Ingredients:

I tsp any kind of oil; 6 spring onions, sliced; I leek, sliced; 2 fresh chillis, finely sliced; 1/2 tsp five spice powder; I pint (20 fl oz/600ml) stock; I packet dried noodles; 2 tsp cherry jam.

METHOD:

Heat the oil in a saucepan and fry the onions, leek and chillis, sprinkling with the five spice powder. When they begin to brown, pour on the stock. Once the stock has reached a simmer, add the noodles. As the noodles soften, stir in the cherry jam and allow to dissolve. As soon as the noodles are cooked, serve in a large tureen with floating cherry blossom as a garnish.

Serves 2–4.

SUMMER SPECIALS

Perhaps one reason the Japanese are so appreciative of seasons other than summer is that summer is not quite such an ideal season there as it can be in the more temperate climate of Europe. Heat and very high humidity are real problems of the Japanese summer, and in the crowded big cities this can make the warm months very uncomfortable.

Japanese foods reflect this by being not just cold, but cooling in their very nature. A particular type of shredded gelatine made from seaweed, called "kanten", is not just delicious, but utterly cooling as it slips down the throat. It is available in Japanese and some Chinese restaurants and also from Oriental stores.

Bean curd has a similar light, cool texture and is served a great deal in the summer, especially cold as part of a salad. Since bean curd is extremely low-calorie, this is another helpful point for slimmers.

Particular foods in season during the summer months include fish. The freshwater river trout (called "ayu" in Japanese) is a summer favourite there as well as here. In Britain you should find it easy to get hold of farmed rainbow trout at this time of the year, but if you can find it (especially if you have an angling friend) the brown trout is even better.

In Japan tuna (called "katsuo") is another favourite fish, and the English equivalent would be salmon. The Japanese like to eat tuna lightly cooked or marinated with a horseradish dip. Surprisingly enough this is actually a very similar dish and combination of flavours to the British habit of having poached salmon with horseradish or hollandaise sauce at this time of the year. You can celebrate the season by sticking to the British version, but for a change why not substitute fresh tuna in the recipe given below for Poached Salmon or Tuna.

In many of the world's hot and humid countries people have discovered that eating highly spicy "hot" tasting foods can actually have a cooling effect. In India curry is the ingredient which causes perspiration to spring from the forehead – with the cooling effect that follows. In Japan hot tastes are also used, but in far milder and rather sweeter versions which I think taste much pleasanter. Radish, ginger, spring onion and horseradish are the "hots" used liberally to garnish cold salads of noodles and bean curd – a really unusual and delicious taste sensation.

It's also surprising to discover that it was the Japanese who invented the flavoured crushed ice our children know and adore under the name "slush". You may associate it with Disneyworld and all things American, but in fact slush was originally a very upmarket exclusive treat to cool the Japanese upper classes on hot days.

This is because it was invented before refrigeration, and therefore had to be made from natural ice saved from the winter. The ice was "farmed" in special ponds and then stored in insulated ice houses. Most of course thawed, but the remainder was crushed up and then flavoured with strawberry, lemon or melon syrup to make slush – called "kakigo" in Japanese. The natural winter ice is still farmed in one or two places in Japan and, called "tennengori", it is served in drinks in upmarket bars.

Summer Recipes

River Trout

Ingredients:
4 small trout (preferably brown trout); 2 tsp horseradish sauce; 4 strips nori. Baste of: 2 cloves garlic, crushed; 2 tsp soy sauce; 2 tsp olive oil.

METHOD:

Clean and gut the trout but leave on the bone with head and tail on. Spread the insides of each fish with horseradish sauce and place one strip of nori in the middle of each. Place on the grill rack. Make small slits in the skin and brush on the baste mix. Grill until cooked (when the eye is opaque) turning occasionally and basting with any remaining mix. Fish do not take long to cook, so be careful not to overdo them. Since this dish is not a complete balanced meal in itself, I suggest you serve it with plain boiled rice and spring greens.

Serves 4.

Fresh Tuna Salad

Ingredients:

2 medium-size fresh tuna steaks; sesame oil; sea salt; ½ head Chinese leaves. Dressing of: 2 tsp lemon juice; I tsp any kind of vinegar; 3 tsp olive oil; I tsp any kind of sugar; I clove garlic, crushed; soy sauce to taste.

METHOD:

Coat the tuna steaks in the sesame oil and rub on a little ground sea salt. Place under the grill and cook until crisping slightly at the edges, turning the steaks and re-coating with oil and salt as necessary. Put to one side. Roughly shred the Chinese leaves into a salad bowl. Remove the cooked and cooled tuna from the bowl and flake into small pieces. Add to the salad bowl. Pour on the dressing and toss all thoroughly together, sprinkling with soy sauce to taste. For speed (if you just want a quick lunch for example) you can substitute canned tuna in oil. Add straight to the Chinese leaves from the tin, adjusting the quantity of oil in the dressing if the tuna is tinned in oil. If tinned in brine, drain first.

Serves 2–4.

Poached Salmon or Tuna

Ingredients:

4 large fresh salmon or tuna steaks; light stock (enough to cover fish); 4 tbsp mayonnaise; 2 tbsp horseradish sauce; 1 inch/2.5cm piece fresh root ginger, peeled and diced very finely.

METHOD:

Place the salmon or tuna steaks in the stock and simmer very gently until the fish is lightly cooked. You will see the colour change and the flakes begin to separate very slightly. Carefully remove from the stock and put aside to cool. Mix the mayonnaise and horseradish sauce. Place the steaks on a serving dish and pour on the sauce. Sprinkle ginger over the top. Since this dish is not a complete main course in itself I suggest you serve it with hot noodles, or for a more Western-style dish, new potatoes and peas.

Serves 4.

Chilled Noodle Salad

Ingredients:

1 packet cellophane noodles; sesame oil; 1/2 cucumber, cut into matchsticks; 6 spring onions, sliced; 1 pack watercress; 1 small can water chestnuts, sliced. Dressing of: soy sauce; vinegar; sesame oil; sake, brown sugar and five spice powder to taste.

METHOD:

Cook the noodles, drain, stir in a dribble of oil to stop them sticking as they cool, and put to one side. Mix up your dressing, adjusting quantities to suit your taste – some people like this salad to taste quite strongly of the soy sauce, others prefer a more Western oil and vinegar flavour. Put all the vegetables in a salad bowl and toss thoroughly together in the dressing. Leave in the fridge to chill for about 1 hour – the idea is that the cellophane noodles absorb the dressing and go a lovely golden brown colour. Serve when chilled.

Serves 2–4.

Chilled Tofu with Garnish

Ingredients:
1 packet bean curd; 4 spring onions; 2 fresh chillis; 2 cloves garlic; 2 inch/5cm piece fresh root ginger, peeled; 1 tsp sesame oil.

METHOD:
Drain the bean curd and place in a large, shallow serving dish. Make intersecting cuts across the bean curd, so that it is cubed, but still more or less arranged in a square. Put in the fridge while you make the garnish. Chop the spring onions, chillis, garlic and ginger finely and fry them vigorously in the oil until they are lightly toasted. Sprinkle onto the bean curd and serve immediately.

Serves 1 as a main course, 2 as a side dish.

Home-made Japanese Sorbet or Slush

Ingredients:
1 small melon; 2–3 tbsp any kind of sugar; 1 tray very forzen ice cubes.

METHOD:
Peel and deseed the melon and liquidise to a pulp. Place the pulp in a heavy-bottomed pan together with the sugar and bring to the boil, stirring continuously. Reduce to a syrup, adding more sugar if necessary. Put to one side to cool. Crush the ice. You can either use a purpose-made ice crusher, or put the ice in a couple of plastic bags and bash it with a rolling pin until it is thoroughly crushed. Pile the ice in serving dishes and pour on the cold melon syrup. Serve, with a sprinkling of icing sugar if desired. Fruit syrups are very popular in China and Japan, and in many Oriental supermarkets there is a wide range of ready-made syrups of guava, melon, etc, which you can use for convenience.

Serves 2–4.

AUTUMN DELIGHTS

I think we have forgotten how to enjoy autumn in Britain. A few years ago harvest festival was still an important feature of the year, when everybody enjoys the idea of all the good food of the season's crop. Michaelmas daisies, asters, chrysanthemums and dahlias were in the flower shops. Stuffed marrows, fresh baked bread, new-season apples with cheese, baked potatoes, loads and loads of different vegetable and mushroom dishes all seemed to be around to make the mouth water with anticipation of a season of filling foods. In America, Thanksgiving continues the tradition and is a wonderful celebration of the marvellous seasonal food available, but sadly in Britain all we seem to have imported from the US are plastic pumpkins and trick-or-treat. It's all a long way from Keats's vision of mellow fruitfulness.

In Japan, autumn provides the opportunity for everybody to draw breath after the humidity of the summer, and as the weather changes the Japanese enjoy the simple, stark beauty of the colder landscape.

Many of the Japanese autumn specialities are similar to those popular in Europe — especially the passion for mushrooms. While the Europeans are out looking for truffles and ceps (what we call "penny bun") the Japanese are hunting up matsutake. These giant mushrooms grow in the pine woods. Their white clean texture and exquisite pine-like fragrance make them highly popular, and the first matsutake of the year are used for high-class gifts or served at top-class restaurants. Matsutake is popularly used with rice. Just as with truffles, even a small amount of matsutake gives rice a deep, mellow flavour and minced matsutake is often mixed into a dish just before serving — again very similar to the Italian way of grating shreds of truffle onto a risotto at the last minute. You should be able to find dried matsutake at Oriental stores, so why not treat yourself? Otherwise you can substitute ordinary mushrooms in the risotto recipe given below.

In the days before freezers British housewives used to spend the autumn bottling, jamming and pickling until there wasn't a container left in the house. It was the same in Japan, and the Japanese taste for eating a variety of different pickles at this time of year continues. One of the nicest Oriental pickles – a mild white cabbage pickle – is very widely available both in supermarkets and at Oriental stores, so the recipe I have given uses this one, but there is a huge variety of alternatives. In fact, so important is the honest pickle, that the Japanese even have a saying: "When the pickle ['kim chee' in Japanese] is ready, then winter can come."

Autumn Recipes

Mushroom Risotto

Ingredients:
4 large dried matsutake mushrooms (see Method); 250g/8oz raw round grain rice; 1 large onion, chopped; any kind of oil; teriyaki sauce; stock.

METHOD:
Chop and soak the matsutake mushrooms. (If you cannot get them, use any fresh mushroom but try to find really fragrant varieties rather than just button mushrooms). You will need about 125–180g/4–6oz.) Part-boil the rice until the grains are just beginning to swell, drain and set to one side. In a deep frying pan, fry the onion in a little oil until transparent. Drain the mushrooms and place in between two sheets of kitchen towel; pat dry. Add the mushrooms to the onion and stir together for a minute. Now add the rice and stir briefly. Season with teriyaki sauce to taste and add enough stock to keep the bottom of the pan well covered and stop the rice sticking. Allow to simmer until the rice has finished cooking (about 5 minutes), adding more stock if necessary to allow the rice to swell fully.

Serves 2 as a main course or 4 as a side dish.

Pickles and Noodles

Ingredients:
1 small jar pickled cabbage (or any choice of pickle); 1 packet dried noodles; 1 pint (20 fl oz/600ml) stock.

METHOD:
This is a very simple recipe for a quick lunch, a cold salad or an easily prepared side dish. Just cook the noodles in the stock – or use a pack of instant noodle soup if you prefer. Drain the noodles and top with pickles to your taste.
Serves 1 as main course, 2 as side dish.

Hot Pepper Rice

Ingredients:
Approx. 1 cup raw round grain rice per person; any kind of oil; fresh chillis to taste, chopped; 1 red or green pepper (capsicum) per person, sliced.

METHOD:
Cook and drain the rice and stir-fry in the oil in a deep pan together with the chillis and peppers. This goes very well with cold meat for a quick meal.
Serves 1.

Oriental Stuffed Marrow

Ingredients:
1 large marrow; 300g/10oz round grain raw rice; 250g/8oz pork fillet; 2 small onions, chopped; 1 tbsp sesame oil; a pinch of five spice powder; 1–2 tbsp hoisin sauce.

METHOD:

Preheat the oven on medium and put the marrow inside just as it is. Part-cook the rice until it is just beginning to swell, and drain. Mince the pork (or whizz it in a blender). Fry the onions in the oil, adding the pork mince and seasoning with the five spice powder. Cook until the pork releases its juices and begins to change colour. Stir in hoisin sauce to taste; I like it quite strong and use a couple of tablespoonsful. Add the rice and keep stirring. By this time the marrow in the oven will be partly cooked. Remove it from the oven, split it down the middle and scoop out the seeds – this is much simpler to do when the marrow is part-cooked. Place the bottom half of the marrow in a deep casserole. Fill in the hollow with the mince and rice mixture – you will probably have enough to spill out all round the marrow, which is fine. Put the upper half of the marrow back on top and put the lid on the casserole. Return to the oven, turn up to high and leave for about 20 minutes. In practice it will cook happily without spoiling for a lot longer than this, so this is a good dish to serve if you are not exactly sure what time you will be eating.

Serves 2–4.

WINTER WARMERS

It is often surprising to Westerners to discover that winters can be quite harsh, especially in certain parts of Japan. We tend to think of light kimonos, sandals and delicately built houses that seem to have much more to do with a tropical climate. But Japan is not a tropical country. The northern tip of Japan is at the same latitude as Peking, renowned for its freezing winters. So winter can be just as tough on the Japanese as on anyone else. It is a time for wrapping up in quilted clothes – the traditionalists wear wonderful quilted silk coats around the house – taking lots of long hot soaks in the bath tub, and of course, eating plenty of steaming hot foods. Stews and other one-pot dishes, often cooked at the table, are a feature of Japanese winter food. In the past very few fresh vegetables were available, and preserved, salted and pickled foods were very much a feature of winter celebration menus. Nowadays food importing and freezers mean the traditional winter foods are rather less popular. But one Japanese winter favourite is the same as ours – the tangerine. Symbolic of the sun and full of much needed healthy vitamins, tangerines pop up everywhere in winter Japan.

Winter Recipes

Hot Pot Noodles

Ingredients:
1 packet dried noodles; any leftovers, eg, ham, cold peas, Tokyo Omelette (recipe p. 113), prawns etc; 2 tbsp sake; 1 tbsp soy sauce.

METHOD:
This very typical and easy-to-make winter warming dish is a user-up of leftovers. Just prepare the noodles as directed on the packet and towards the end of the cooking process throw the rest of the ingredients into the pan. Simmer it all together briefly for a minute or two to evaporate most of the water. Ideally you want a noodle stew without too much liquid. If it is too sloppy it will be difficult to eat.
    Serves 1–2.

Japanese Stew

Ingredients:
50ml/2 fl oz soya oil; 1 fresh chilli, chopped; 175g/6oz tin bamboo shoots, drained; 2 small chicken breasts, cut into slices across the

grain; 2 broccoli florets, sliced; approx. 175 ml/6 fl oz stock; 4 tbsp sweet sherry; 4 tbsp any kind of sugar; 4 tbsp soy sauce; 1 tbsp preserved stem ginger.

METHOD:
Heat the oil in a deep frying pan and fry the chilli and bamboo shoots for a minute, then add the chicken. When the chicken is well sealed, add the broccoli, turning it over gently until it becomes bright green and shiny. Add the rest of the ingredients and stir thoroughly. Leave on a gentle simmer for 15–20 minutes, stirring occasionally. If you want to thicken the sauce at the end, remove a little liquid from the pan and allow to cool before blending it with 2 tsp cornflour and stirring back into the pan.

Serves 2–4.

Twice Cooked Rice

Ingredients:
Sesame oil; cooked leftover rice; whole cloves of garlic; teriyaki sauce; hoisin sauce; cooked beef (or any other leftover meat), finely chopped.

METHOD:
Since this is another leftovers dish, quantities aren't important; it is really a matter of what you want to use up. Take a deep earthenware or porcelain individual rice pot (see page 124) or a large mug or earthenware cocotte dish if you do not have a proper rice pot. Grease it with a little oil and put in a layer of rice and then a garlic clove. Sprinkle generously with teriyaki sauce and a dollop of hoisin. Top with a layer of meat, and then repeat the whole process. Keep adding layers until you have filled one pot per person. Using individual pots is not only authentically Oriental, it makes the reheating process much easier to control. Put the pot (or pots) in a steamer and steam thoroughly for 15–20 minutes. The ingredients

by then will have melded together, but you can cook them longer if you like. Eat straight from the pot.

Tangerine Salad

Ingredients:
6–8 tangerines; 1 small head curly kale or savoy cabbage. Dressing of: soy sauce; sesame oil; vinegar; any kind of sugar (amounts adjusted to taste).

METHOD:
Peel and segment the tangerines, reserving the best bits of peel. Shred the cabbage finely and put in a large salad bowl with the tangerines. Toss thoroughly in the dressing. Cut up the tangerine peel into very fine slivers and sprinkle 2 tsp onto the salad. Serve. Keep any leftover peel slivers drying in a jar in the fridge – they make excellent cooking flavourings and a garnish for other dishes.
    Serves 4.

FESTIVE COOKING

Like the rest of us, the Japanese enjoy breaking up the year with special festivals, and food is of course a major part of any festival. Much traditional Japanese festival food is rather too unusual for Western tastes – and it has to be said it is declining in popularity in Japan as well. The equivalent in Britain would be the way many people are now turning away from traditional old-fashioned dishes like Christmas pudding and swapping to lighter choices instead. So, although I have described some of the old-fashioned Japanese dishes for those who want to be truly authentic, I think if you want to try a Japanese-style celebration you should choose the modern versions to begin with anyway.

The New Year

New Year is the most important festive season in the Japanese calendar. Just as in Britain at Christmas time you might give someone a special Christmas hamper, so the Japanese give each other New Year's food gifts. Called "osechi-ryori" in Japanese, an assortment of little delicacies is piled into beautiful lacquer trays which stack one on top of the other – again a little like the custom of stocking a hamper with lots of different foods.

The lacquer trays are called "jubako". Within families the housewife used to prepare three trays for each person in the family and they could eat them over the holiday period – rather like we might give someone a box of chocolates or dates. These family jubako were handed down from generation to generation and are now collector's items, but you can get modern ones at Oriental shops (see Where to Buy pages 48–9)

Nowadays most boxes of New Year food are bought ready-made from the big stores – again, just like ordering a hamper. The contents are much more Westernised. Instead of kelp and dried anchovies you're more likely to come across prawns, cold meats and sushi. When you're preparing your Christmas and New Year goodies this year, why not get hold of a lacquer tray and lay out a few delicacies – they make marvellous canapés to hand round at a Christmas drinks party.

Another New Year favourite is "datemaki", a type of fish omelette which is delicious, and makes a wonderful snack meal to eat during the season.

New Year Recipes

A Japanese-style Platter

This is a Westernised version of Japanese osechi-ryori which you can lay out on a lacquer tray for comment-provoking party canapés.

Ingredients:

1 pack bean curd, drained; 2 cloves garlic, crushed; 6 rice cakes; 12 large cooked prawns; soy sauce, 12 Medjool dates; 2 rolls Tokyo Omelette (see recipe p.113); teriyaki sauce; 6 slices smoked salmon; lemon juice; 4 slices nori; 2 packets Japanese Rice Crackers.

METHOD:

Put the bean curd in the blender together with the garlic. Purée together to make a smooth cream. Cut each rice cake in half and spread with a little of the mixture. Cut prawns down the centre line into "butterflies" and place a prawn on top of each rice cake half. Sprinkle with a little soy sauce and arrange on the tray. Halve and stone the dates and fill with the tofu mix. Add to the tray. Slice up the omelette rolls into cross-sections and sprinkle with teriyaki sauce; add to the tray. Lay the smoked salmon slices flat on a board and sprinkle with lemon juice. Place a nori strip on top of each slice and roll into a sausage. Cut the rolls into bite-size pieces and secure with a cocktail stick. Add to tray. Finally fill in any gaps with a sprinkling of Japanese Rice Crackers.

Datemaki Omelette

Ingredients:

2 boil-in-bag cod steaks; 4 eggs; 2 tbsp soy sauce; 1 tbsp sweet sherry; soya oil.

METHOD:

Cook the cod steaks as directed on the packet. Break the eggs into a bowl and whisk with the soy sauce and sherry. Break the cod steaks into flakes and mix into the egg mixture. Heat an omelette pan and grease with a little oil. Pour in enough mixture to make a thin omelette. Cook until firm and then roll into a tube. Put to one side and repeat the process until you have used all the mixture. You can either serve the omelettes hot as they are, or cool them and then cut them into slices to serve as snacks or garnish, which is how the Japanese have them. They also tend to use only the egg yolk for the omelette, but this can be rather rich.

FESTIVAL FUN

Apart from New Year there are various festivals throughout the year in Japan. On February 4 Setsubun Eve approximates to Hallowe'en in the West. On this night the Japanese have a tradition of throwing roasted soya beans out of the doorway, shouting: "Oni wa soto. Fuku wa uchi," or "Go away, devils. Come in, good fortune."

Children have their own special days in Japan as well. The Girls' Festival is on March 3 and the Boys' on May 5 – so I have put in a recipe that might amuse your children and make a bit of a change for you.

One of the nicest Japanese traditions is the custom of "moon viewing" or "otsuki-mi" in Japanese. This happens round about August 15 when the Japanese go out at night to admire the light of the full moon. Some sleep outdoors, and the more poetic like to meditate and maybe feel inspired to write a short poem or "haiku" in Japanese. Special round rice cakes are made to resemble full moons. It is very characteristic of the Japanese to take time out to notice the natural beauty around them – and something I think we could learn from in the West, so I've included an August recipe to remind you to relax and enjoy a summer night once in a while.

Festival Recipes

Bean Rice

Ingredients:
150g/5oz dried soya beans (soaked overnight in cold water); 150g/5oz dried aduki beans (soaked overnight in cold water);

350g/12oz raw short grain rice; 2 tbsp sake or any kind of sherry; 1 tbsp soy sauce.

METHOD:
Put both lots of beans and their soaking liquid into a saucepan and bring to the boil. Cover the pan and simmer for 1 hour until tender. Drain and reserve the bean cooking liquid. Put the beans in a dish and keep warm. Cook the rice in the bean liquid (adding more water if necessary). When rice is nearly cooked through, stir in the beans and the other ingredients and finish cooking. Serve with a salad or vegetables.
    Serves 3–4.

Snap, Crack and Pop

This crispy rice dish is adored by children, but it can be slightly difficult to get the rice really puffy and popping until you become experienced. Tesco sells rice that is pre-puffed (see page 42) or you can make the dish using popping corn instead, which it is much easier to get to puff.

A few days before you need it, slightly overcook your rice and leave it uncovered in the fridge to dry out. Heat some oil in a heavy-bottomed pan and when it is beginning to smoke, add a sprinkling of rice. The rice should snap, crack and pop. When it has puffed, put it aside to keep warm in a dish. Keep repeating the process until you have finished your rice. Be very careful not to let the oil get too warm. When it is all done, serve with dipping sauce poured over the top.
Dipping sauce:
Mix together: 4 tbsp soy sauce; 4 tbsp teriyaki sauce; 1 tbsp brown sugar; 1 tbsp hoisin sauce.

August Moons

Like the rest of these festive dishes, August moons are really a bit of fun for your children. The idea is for the children to make them themselves to look like different phases of the moon.

Get out as many rice cakes as you think you will need (allow extra in case some get broken or messed up) and have ready the following toppings: smoked salmon slices; thin sliced ham; hard-boiled egg in slices. You or your children can use a round pastry cutter to cut the salmon and ham into rounds about the same size as the rice cakes. Sprinkle a rice cake with soy sauce or lemon juice and place a round of smoked salmon on it, slightly off-centre so that a crescent of rice cake shows round one side. Hey-presto, it's a new moon. Take a ham round and cut in half – yes you've guessed, turn the next rice cake into a half-moon. Carry on experimenting until you have used up all the ingredients. Either eat as you go along, or put to one side ready for a family meal.

THE TEA CEREMONY

Perhaps the first thing we all associate with Japan is the Japanese tea ceremony. The image of the beautiful geisha in her decorative silk kimono delicately handing round porcelain bowls of tea to people seated on a cane tatami mat is one that is inseparable from the Western view of Japanese culture.

In fact the charming ritual was actually imported from China originally. Today the tea ceremony is still very important in Japan – and far from the tourist gimmick one might imagine it to be. Even modern young Japanese girls still consider being able to perform the tea ceremony well an important accomplishment in the marriage stakes – rather like being a good cook was in Britain until the arrival of the "new man".

Essentially the tea ceremony is the art of preparing tea as gracefully as possible, but the manner in which it is done is highly formalised. Practitioners must strictly observe the correct procedures, such as how to pour the water and hold the tea bowl. The tea used for the tea ceremony is a special type of powdered green tea called "matcha". After adding hot water to the powder, it is whipped with a bamboo whisk which looks rather like a shaving brush. The taste is bitter, but refreshing.

Japanese green tea has recently become very popular as a health ingredient. It is rich in anti-oxidants and mildly diuretic. These properties mean it is useful for slimmers on a weight "plateau" as well as being excellent for the complexion. For more details see page 40.

Because of the philosophical disciplines involved in the ceremony it is often used as an introduction to Zen Buddhism for visitors at Zen monasteries. Fortunately you don't need to be a Zen monk to appreciate the elegance and simplicity of the tea ceremony. And the special food that goes with it is delicious whether or not you attempt the ceremony itself.

Tea ceremony food, "kaiseki", is the most refined in Japanese cuisine with great emphasis being placed on simplicity and harmony. The tastes, textures and colours of the food should balance one another and the containers in which it is served should enhance its appearance. Kaiseki food reflects the seasons and if possible is locally produced; it should not be expensive or extravagant, but should be imaginative and in good taste.

If you want to throw your own Japanese-style afternoon tea party, many of the recipes given here – for example August Moons or the New Year canapés, will work excellently as your version of kaiseki food, or as you get more used to all the different ingredients of Japanese food, you could experiment with your own recipes.

11

EATING OUT AND RESTAURANTS

Eating Out Japanese

With the help of this book and all its recipes, eating out Japanese
should now be a piece of cake, or should that be bean curd? You
will be familiar with all the main restaurant dishes and from knowing
the ingredients you will be able to pick the ones you like, and if you
are slimming, that fit in with your diet. The dishes you are most likely
to find on the menu are: tempura; teppan yaki or yaki tori; sukiyaki;
teriyaki; sushi and sashimi. As you know, all these are included on
the Japanese Diet, so you don't need to avoid them. However if
you are slimming very strictly, you might want to save tempura for
special occasions only, as it is deep-fried.

Most Japanese restaurants tend to be like Chinese restaurants in
serving a variety of dishes together. So you may find that a bowl
of soup (usually miso soup) comes along with the main course
you have chosen, even if you didn't ask for soup. Other Japanese
restaurants are more Westernised and you may be offered a few
sushi for starters, followed by say teriyaki or yaki tori for a main
course served with rice. I think this type of menu is a good
choice for your first adventures in eating out Japanese, but later
on you'll probably be tucking into a working day lunch of sashimi
accompanied by miso broth just like any Tokyo "office lady"!

When Westerners go into a Chinese or Japanese restaurant
and order fried rice the waiters can tell immediately that they

are dealing with people who know nothing about Oriental food. So if you want to impress the waiter, order your rice plain boiled. Another trick picked up in Asia is to turn the lid of the tea pot over when you want it refilled with fresh tea – just try these and you'll see how impressed your friends will be by the extra-attentive service you get.

One word of warning – Japanese restaurants in Britain have a reputation for being expensive, and many are sticking to the tradition, so be prepared.

JAPANESE RESTAURANTS

This is just a selection of the huge number of Japanese restaurants that have sprung up in London and country-wide. Most serve sushi, and they are not all as expensive as the first wave of Japanese restaurants in London used to be. It is a good idea to phone first as the opening hours are not always what one would expect – many are closed on a Monday, while some close on a Sunday or even a Saturday! If you are having any difficulty finding the ingredients you need for cooking at home, the restaurants can be very helpful in putting you in touch with suppliers. Some even have shops attached to them, so do give your local Japanese restaurant a call even if you are not planning to eat there.

London
Ajimura, 51/53 Shelton Street, London WC2. Tel: 0171 240 9424. Trendy Soho sushi bar which was one of the first to get started. Big for advertising, film and media crowd.
Akasaka, 10a Golders Green Road, London NW11. Tel: 0181 455 0676. Sushi bar which represents yet another outbreak of North London Orientalism.
Aykoku-Kaku, Bucklersbury House, 9 Walbrook, London EC4N.

Tel: 0171 236 9020. City restaurant in the tradition of Tokyo fast food. Not only has a sushi and a teppan yaki bar but also provides o-bento (take-away) delivery to office workers, just like in Japan. Closed at the weekend.

Benihana, 77 Kings Road, London SW3. Tel: 0171 376 7799. Branch of the well-known, more or less global, chain of teppan yaki bars which has become very fashionable for the glitterati and ladies who lunch.

Dan Dan, 333 Putney Bridge Road, London SW15. Tel: 0181 780 1953. West London sushi bar.

Fuji, 36–40 Brewer Street, London W1. Tel: 0171 734 0957. One of the very first of the Soho Japanese restaurants, and still one of the best.

Masako, 6 St Christopher's Place, London W1. Tel: 0171 486 1399. Sushi bar just off Oxford Street which also has traditional tatami rooms for hire for small parties.

Matsuri St James's, 15 Bury Street, London W1. Tel: 0171 839 1101. Serving sushi and teppan yaki, this is one of the Japanese restaurants that helped get the cuisine its reputation for excellence – and expense.

Mitsukoshi, Dorland House, 14–20 Lower Regent Street, London SW1. Tel: 0171 930 0317. Another very posh restaurant, with private tatami rooms available.

Pret à Manger, branches throughout London. Tel: Not a specialist Japanese chain but provides Japanese lunches to take away for London office workers.

Saga, 43 South Molton Street, London W1. Tel: 0171 629 3931. Sushi bar popular with fashion victims who lunch there after a visit to Brown's designer clothing store.

Suntory, 72 St James's Street, London SW1. Tel: 0171 409 0201. One of the originals and still one of the best. Sushi, teppan yaki, tatami rooms.

South
Kosaido Nippon Kan, Longmoor Road, Liphook, Hants. Tel: 01428 724555.

South-West
Samurai, 1B Chandos Road, Redland, Bristol. Tel: 01179 742816.

Midlands
Higoi, 57 Lenton Boulevard, Nottingham, Notts. Tel: 01159 423379.

North
Youna, 52 Portland Street, Manchester. Tel: 0161 236 0783.
Koreana, Kings House, 40a King Street West, Manchester. Tel: 0161 832 4330.

Wales
Chikako's, 10–11 Mill Lane, Cardiff. Tel: 01222 665279.

Scotland
Yumi, 2 West Courts, Edinburgh. Tel: 0131 337 2173.

Northern Ireland
The Ginger Tree, 29 Bally Robert Road, Ballyclare, Belfast. Tel: 01232 848176.

Eire
Shiro, Ahakista (a small village), County Cork, Eire. Tel: 00353 2767030.
Ayumi-Ya, Newpark Centre, Newtonpark Avenue, Blackrock, Dublin, Eire. Tel: 00353 1283 1767.

Eating Out Oriental

One of the things the Japanese and the British have in common is that we are both island nations, and like most island peoples we are constantly being visited by ships from all over the world. Of course, the Chinese mainland was the nearest and most obvious place from where visitors arrived and they certainly brought strong influences not only in cuisine but in philosophy as well. So Japanese food obviously has many similarities with Chinese food, but the Japanese were also open to other influences which never penetrated the vast recesses of mainland China. In the 16th and early 17th centuries there were particularly strong links with the Portuguese and Spanish (James Clavell's well researched novels give an interesting fictionalised account of this period). But during the Edo period (from the mid-17th to the mid-19th centuries) Japan went through a period of insularity and austerity during which it shunned contact with the rest of the world and in which tradition and ritual became stultified and change was resisted. It is really only since World War II that Japan has truly emerged from this period and change is happening very fast now.

Today the cuisine as we know it is largely the product of that early period of exposure to influences followed by a time of great rigidity. This is what gives it its unique, contradictory, combination of simplicity, lightness and yet excitement and variety of tastes. Chinese cookery, on the other hand, has evolved along very different lines since the middle-ages when the two cuisines were so much more alike.

Because of the large and continuing emigration from Hong Kong and China over the years, there has been a tremendous interchange between Chinese and Western cookery. This has resulted in the heavier, more "junky" sweet sauced dishes becoming a more prominent part of Chinese cookery. Sadly this is far from authentic to real Chinese cookery. When you are eating out in a Chinese restaurant try to think a little Japanese and you will get a much better impression of true Chinese cuisine. Remember, in every great cuisine, whether Western or Oriental, the recipe as a whole must remain true to the main ingredient of the dish — thus a beef dish should taste predominantly of beef, not of toffee or pineapple or whatever "garnish" ingredient is included in the recipe. So if you are eating a sweet and sour dish whose major ingredient is unidentifiable, you are not eating genuine Chinese (or any other cuisine for that matter). The big difference between Japanese and

Chinese food is that the Japanese almost never fall into that trap, whereas it is all too easy to find that kind of dish when eating Chinese.

Eating Out: Other Oriental Cuisines

The main Oriental cuisines are:

1. **Chinese, divided into Peking, Cantonese, Szechuan and Shanghai (rare in Britain)** Peking is regarded as the gourmet cuisine with the greatest variety of ingredients, recipes and cooking techniques. If you are slimming it is wise to avoid Peking food. Cantonese food is very widespread, originating from South China and largely associated with peasant food, though at its best it rivals Peking. Cantonese specialises in vegetable stir-frys and seafood, both of which are good dishes for a slimmer to choose. Szechuan food tends to be very hot and spicy, with a lot of heavily salted or chilli dishes. It is not ideal for a slimmer or anyone with digestive problems, but it makes a great treat once in a while. Shanghai is the source of many of the Buddhist and Taoist vegetarian dishes so influential in Japanese cooking, excellent for slimmers.
2. **Thai** Like Chinese, Thai food is very wide-ranging. The best dishes for the slimmer to choose are those lightly cooked but relying on flavour and fragrance rather than sauces. Fragrant rice and lemon grass dishes are a good choice.
3. **Vietnamese** There are now increasing numbers of Vietnamese and Korean restaurants in Britain specialising in dishes which are reminiscent of Chinese but usually much lighter and less heavily sauced and seasoned. Typical Vietnamese techniques include wrapping cooked meats in large chilled lettuce leaves (rather than the pancake roll the Chinese would use). This means Vietnamese is an excellent cuisine for the slimmer.

Eating Out Western

Obviously for the first four weeks that you are on the Japanese Diet, you will not want to eat Western food. But later on, when you have returned to largely Western eating, while incorporating the nutrition tips you have discovered on the Japanese Diet, it is useful to know how to pick the foods which are most in keeping with the Japanese approach to eating. And, of course, it's useful to know in case you are in a position where you must eat Western during the Japanese Diet.

What to order French Plain grilled fish; steak; salads; soups; casseroles. Avoid rich, heavily sauced old-fashioned "haute cuisine". Look for "cuisine minceur".

What to order Italian Vegetable dishes; plain pasta dishes. Avoid deep-fried dishes or pasta with rich cream sauces. Cut back on the parmesan. No pizza.

What to order in a steakhouse Plain grilled steak with vegetables. No chips; ask for low-fat spread or cottage cheese to put on your baked potato. Plenty of salad, but stick to low-fat or vinaigrette dressing, no blue cheese. No deep-fried seafood or onion rings. Avoid pudding; ask for fruit salad and ice cream.

What to order take-away

- Don't have pizza.
- Don't have burgers.
- Don't have dona kebab (too fatty).
- Don't have onion bahji.
- Don't have pancake (spring) rolls.
- Don't have sweet and sour pork.
- Don't have chips.
- Do have baked potatoes.
- Do have plain grilled lamb or chicken kebab.
- Do have fish.
- Do have rice.
- Do have curry.
- Do have stir-fry vegetables (eg, beansprouts, chop suey).

PART THREE

12

JAPANESE STRESS BUSTERS

INTRODUCTION

Modern Japanese society is amongst the most stressful in the world. Anybody who has ever travelled on the Tokyo underground and experienced the activities of the professional "pushers" – people specifically employed literally to cram passengers into the carriages – needs no persuading that Tokyo is the most crowded, rushed and urbanised of modern cities. It makes our much-complained-about London Underground's Northern Line look positively calm and relaxing by comparison.

To people who have admired Japanese arts and culture it is a strange paradox that a nation which values tranquillity, contemplation and personal space so highly has produced an urban society which represents the very antithesis of those values.

The Japanese have a concept called "wa" – loosely translated as "personal harmony" – which represents each individual's right to personal space and freedom from anxiety undisturbed by the activities of others. Being physically loaded into a confined space with other people in conditions in which animals would never be allowed to travel must surely count as the most total disruption possible of one's personal wa.

So how on earth do the Japanese cope with the stressful realities of living in later twentieth-century Japan? Traditionally a philosophy of life which includes time for relaxation, massage, physical exercise and quiet contemplation is the Japanese way of gaining the inner strength to cope with life's challenges.

You may have heard of Taoism as an Oriental philosophy, which may sound very complicated and rather head in the clouds. In fact the Japanese approach to inner and outer health is extremely down to earth. Basically they realise that unless you have got your inner, emotional, self sorted out, you can't hope to achieve external, physical well-being.

That is a truth anyone who has ever tried and failed with a slimming diet will quickly recognise. It is well nigh impossible to create that slimmer, fitter, healthier new you, if all your energy is being taken up trying to cope with internal turmoil or external stresses. And that's why this section on relaxation and inner well-being is so important to the Japanese Diet as a whole.

Looking slim, well and attractive on the outside and feeling balanced, relaxed and positive on the inside are so closely interwoven that it is vital to work on both together. There is no point assuming, as many slimmers do, that looking good will make you feel good – most find that it is the reverse: it simply isn't possible to start looking good until you are already beginning to feel good. So the rest of this section contains a brief introduction to Japanese ways of working on the inner and outer self together: through relaxation and meditation; through exercise; and through massage. I have also included a few words on Japanese philosophy, which I think is worth at least thinking about, because it will help tremendously in your quest for slimness and good health.

RELAXATION AND MEDITATION

Relaxation is tremendously important for anyone, and the Japanese see a moment of relaxation as a time to bring mind and body

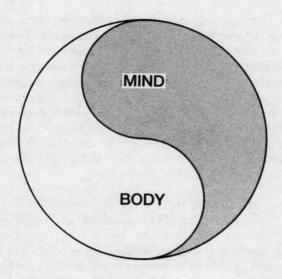

into balance with each other. Since mental stress actually has a number of physical effects on the body, it makes sense to be aware of this link. For example, when someone is under acute stress, a bio-chemical substance called adrenaline is released into the bloodstream. Its function is to prepare the body either to stand and fight the source of stress, or to run away from it (fight or flight). One of the ways it does this is by draining blood out of temporarily non-essential organs like the stomach (which is where that sinking feeling in the pit of your stomach comes from), and then pumping it into important areas like the muscles. Muscles are needed for fighting or fleeing, and to work muscles need oxygen; blood is the pipeline through which oxygen travels round the body.

If the stressed person does have a stand-up fight or really runs away, the adrenaline reaction does its work and switches off naturally. However, in modern society fighting or fleeing are rare. Usually the outward reactions to stress are suppressed and the stress is left unresolved. This means the adrenaline reaction continues to work with no outlet and this can cause real physical problems. The lack of blood supply to the stomach disrupts digestion and can ultimately contribute to ulcers. The diversion of blood to elsewhere in the system results in blood pressure being raised (sometimes permanently) and many doctors believe that this thickening of blood contributes to heart disease.

So there are many reasons why it is so important to deal with stress on a mental and physical level. The first line of attack is to switch off that adrenaline reaction by sending out signals that you no longer need to fight or flee. The best way to do this is by a combination of physical relaxation and mental meditation, and you can start by trying the following exercise.

Centring Meditation

You need no more than five minutes alone to do this exercise; eventually even a couple of moments will be enough. Nobody is too busy or too much in demand to have time to centre. When I was a national newspaper executive I used to retreat to the loo to do my centring meditation, so there are no excuses.

I. Position
Sit comfortably with a straight spine (supported if necessary). Close your eyes. Become aware of your body. Feel its weight as it presses against whatever you are sitting on. Notice which parts of your body are in contact with another surface; sense the feel of that surface on your skin.

2. Breathing
Place your hands gently on your diaphragm – just below your ribcage. Now take a deep breath in, using the air you take in to push up your hands, almost as though your body is a balloon being inflated by the incoming air. Hold it there a second. Now start slowly pushing the air out again. Don't just let it leak out anyhow; use your hands to push it out from your diaphragm, so that air is being pushed out right from the bottom of your

chest and not just the top. Imagine you are squeezing a tube of toothpaste.

The technical term for this is "intercostal diaphragmatic breathing" and it is how professional performers like opera singers, actors and public speakers learn to breathe. Most people breathe very shallowly with just the top part of their chest which means the body has an inadequate exchange of oxygen, causing all sorts of health problems including dizziness and chronic fatigue.

3. Energy

When you are happy with your breathing, start to connect with the flow of energy in your body. As you breathe out, imagine that all the tension in you is being expelled and pushed out along with the breath. Out goes the carbon dioxide, and along with it all the tension in your face, the strains in your muscles, the worries on your mind. When you take your next breath in, be conscious of the new fresh air and oxygen entering your body. Visualise the incoming breath filling right down your whole abdomen, and with it imagine the energy streaming into your body and spreading outwards into your arms and hands.

4. Renewal

So strong will the sense be of the new oxygen flowing into your circulation that your hands will begin to tingle and get warm. Relax your hands and arms; just let them hang as you become aware of the circulation flowing through them.

5. Emerging – passive or active

At this stage your centring process can go two ways, depending whether you want to remain quiet and passive in preparation for further relaxation and sleep, or whether you want to be re-energised with positive action to face an immediate challenge.

Passive Continue to be conscious of your breathing and of the flow of oxygenated blood round your body which your breathing triggers. Gradually increase the pauses between breaths and the length of each breath, so that your breathing rate begins to slow down. Imagine that your heart beat is linked with this and that it too is slowing down. Picture yourself in your favourite relaxing surroundings — a beach, a country walk, a glowing fireside — and allow all your senses to be aware of those surroundings. Hear the surf breaking or the birds singing or the fire crackling. Smell the sea air or the grass or the wood smoke. Run your fingers through the sand, kick your feet in the leaves, feel the warmth of the fire on your face. Stay in your imaginary place as long as you need (or is appropriate) before gradually allowing yourself to come back and continue with your day.

Active Concentrate on the flow of blood into your hands. Now start to feel the energy in your hands. As they tingle and buzz start shaking them, feeling their warmth and aliveness. Rub your palms together and flex your arms. Some people snap their fingers at this stage, which increases the sensation of energy flowing uninterrupted right from your intake of breath to the tips of your fingers. Push back your shoulders and open your chest. Flex the major muscle groups — especially shoulders, back, thighs and arms. Take a good long breath in, and this time push it back out again as quickly and forcefully as you can, using the muscles in your abdomen. Be aware of that centre of strength and energy in your abdomen, and carry that consciousness with you as you go out to face whatever is ahead.

EXERCISE AND T'AI CHI

Controlled exercise is a logical next step in the Oriental and Japanese philosophy of health and well-being. T'ai Chi exercises are typical of the way that mind and body are regarded as one entity. Following on from the centring meditation which can either be used to tranquillise or re-energise, it is interesting to note that while one form of T'ai Chi concentrates on stillness and balance, another is much more active and forms the basis of Oriental martial arts.

Looked at from the outside, much T'ai Chi exercise appears quite meaningless, involving a complicated and convoluted set of postures and movements. If performed correctly, these are in fact both physically and mentally demanding, and can be very gymnastic. But even then the exercises are really a means to an end – and, as ever, that goal is to have a mind and body working in balance and harmony together.

T'ai Chi comes from the ancient Chinese philosophy of Taoism which dates back to before the twelfth century BC and has since spread widely through the Far East and Japan. The controlled movements of T'ai Chi are designed to promote health through posture, breathing and relaxation. Posture is important to bring the body into alignment, while breathing and relaxation help improve functioning of the organs, digestion and oxygenation of the blood circulation.

T'ai Chi is now immensely popular in the West, so look out for classes at your local sports centre. Even if you don't want to go further it is worth bearing in mind the following fundamentals of T'ai Chi in your day-to-day life, especially as you walk around or sit down, and in any sports you do.

1. Posture

A great deal of the chronic fatigue so many of us suffer is largely due to poor posture which causes muscles to be unnaturally tensed for long periods of time. This sort of tension can particularly occur in the shoulders and give rise to persistent headaches and poor sleep.

To improve your posture you first have to let your body get to know what good posture feels like. Stand in profile in front of a mirror with feet hip-width apart. Bend your knees very slightly and untense your thigh muscles (you hadn't noticed how tense they were, had you?). Now tuck your tail under very slightly and start the process of straightening your spine. Imagine each vertebra placed absolutely vertically one on top of the other. When you get to the spine between your shoulders you will notice that you have to bring your shoulder blades back and round, then under in order to get your spine straight. Look at the difference in the mirror. Now think about your neck. Your chin will need to come up slightly and you may have to push your neck back slightly as though pushing into your collar. Now open your chest and breathe and relax. Bounce slightly and settle until you feel comfortable in your new posture. Become aware of how it feels and try to recreate it as much as possible – sitting at your desk, walking down the street, in a bus queue.

2. Rootedness
Deriving directly from posture is a T'ai Chi concept best translated at "rootedness". The best way of explaining it is to feel it. Take your shoes and socks off. Get into your good posture position. Now spread your feet and work your toes into the carpet until your feet have got the best possible grip on the ground. Remember that this planet is a sphere revolving in space and you might very well be on the bottom at this moment. Realise that you haven't fallen off and feel the strength of that connection between your feet and the floor. Feel that strength and power growing all the way up your legs and into your body. That's rootedness, and as they say, you really need to have been there.

3. Abdomen
The abdominal area is regarded as being of immense importance in Oriental philosophy and medicine, and it has its own special name, "hara". From a purely physical or medical point of view this is hardly surprising since many of the body's most important organs and functions are situated here.

If you are not quite sure where we are talking about, then think of the area that is framed by your lower ribs at the top and your hip bones at the bottom, with the naval as the mid-point. This area includes your diaphragm (for breathing); your kidneys; liver; your digestive system and your reproductive system. Unconscious tension and muscular spasm in this area contribute to a host of health problems.

Breathing properly, as described above, is important, as is learning how to release the muscles of the abdomen. Lie on your back with knees bent, hip-width apart. Now press your lower spine into the floor and tilt and curl your pelvis up and in towards your ribs at the same time as breathing out, so that your abdomen caves right in. Would that one's stomach looked like that all the time. Well, the good news is that if you continue with this exercise, eventually it will! Gently unroll again as you breathe in. Repeat the exercise as often as you like. When you get used to the feeling of how your pelvis tilts and your lower spine curves, you will be able to do the exercise standing up as well. It is extremely effective for those with irritable bowel syndrome.

4. Awareness
Awareness is very much an extension of the concepts of rootedness and hara. It emphasises that in everything we do, we should be conscious of the physical entity of our body. Elements like the alignment of the skeleton and the state of the muscles are especially important. Very often it takes a conscious effort to untense a muscle, and if this is not done, the muscle can easily spasm. Being conscious of how you use your body in your daily life, what it takes to perform simple chores, makes a great difference to well-being. People who habitually lift incorrectly, sit badly, or tense up their face, suffer from back problems and headaches which could be prevented by understanding and responding to the body as a physical, mechanical entity. Many people need professional help (from physiotherapists and qualified fitness instructors) to gain body awareness, but you can at least begin to try to understand it right away.

5. Control
The aspect of control really sums up the ideas of mind and body consciousness that are so important in T'ai Chi. The idea is that through a combination of posture, rootedness and awareness – together with meditation and inner awareness – it is possible to achieve a great controlled balance which can direct not just your physical actions but your whole life. Whether or not you agree

with this concept, it is interesting to note just how little control of our physical actions we have in day-to-day life. Just walking around we exert far more force and energy than is necessary. This becomes obvious when you walk into something and all that excess force is turned back on yourself, causing pain (as well as swearing and a bruise). If that wasted energy could be harnessed through physical self-awareness and control, think how much you could do with it – and for a demonstration, just watch a martial arts expert.

As another experiment in control, try throwing something into the waste paper bin, or picking up a chair by one leg, or circling your hands in opposite direction circles at the same time. All these activities require a minimum of co-ordinated control, yet the effort is noticeable. Imagine if you were able to exert that kind of control all the time with no noticeable effort. That is the power of control which T'ai Chi tries to harness – worth thinking about, even if you aren't the next Zen master!

MASSAGE AND SHIATSU

Now immensely popular in the West, shiatsu (literally "shi", finger and "atsu", pressure) is a Japanese physical therapy which has its roots in Oriental medicine and religious, meditation and exercise techniques.

Shiatsu is very common in Japan – husbands and wives, parents and children often treat each other. Self-shiatsu can include scalp massage, sinuses, neck, arms, hands and toes and, of course, the abdomen.

Jane Downer writes in her book, *Shiatsu* (Hodder Headway Lifeguide, 1992): "It is vital for people to learn to help themselves to recognise and accept individual responsibility for their health. Ultimately it is each person's assumption of self-responsibility for their healing and growth processes that is important for creating and maintaining health."

Certainly the Japanese feel that shiatsu massage is an important element of this. Shiatsu is performed with loose clothes on and shoes removed. There are various methods of applying the massage which include:

○ Pressure – perpendicular pressure, pressing down, letting body weight do the work.
○ Rocking – small pushes and releases, letting the body spring back.
○ Shaking – gently shaking out the muscle.
○ Kneading – circular probing motion of thumbs and fingers.
○ Pounding – light tapping/beating with fingers, palm or fist.
○ Stretching – either to another person or individually.

Another important technique is abdominal release, which you can do for yourself, but is easier and more effective if you get someone else to do it for you. Lie down on your back. Place the fingers of one hand on the lower edge of your ribcage. Take a deep breath in. As you breathe out, push your fingers firmly down and round the lip of your ribcage, so that your abdomen is being moved down and away from your ribs. Rest. Repeat two or three times and no more. As you perform this you are likely to hear large gurglings from your digestive system. This means that spasm in your digestive system is being released and the digestion freed up. It is a good sign, and if you suffer from abdominal bloating you will notice a considerable improvement. You may also find that any aches and pains in the lower back subside.

If you are interested in shiatsu, which is now an extremely popular therapy in the West, then read Jane Downer's book and find yourself a local therapist. If you don't want to go that far, but would still like to discover some of the benefits of a shiatsu-style massage, I have outlined a simple self-massage routine below. Unlike normal shiatsu, this massage places emphasis on improving skin tone and slimness, so it is carried out without clothes on. It is especially beneficial for flabby thighs and puffiness and poor skin. You might want to try it after your bath in combination with applying your favourite skin-toning or anti-cellulite product.

Shiatsu-style Skin-toning Self-massage

Stomach
Starting from above the waist and working downward, lightly stroke the stomach alternating with the palms and fingers. To complete the massage, slowly push four fingers of each hand into the hip and thigh area where the legs join the torso.

Waist
Place both hands on the lower back, then move them forward around the waistline and push fat towards the pit of the stomach. Move both hands simultaneously.

Buttocks
Push four fingers of each hand slowly into the fold under the buttocks. Then slowly move your hands upwards, using the whole of each hand. If you use a massager, move upwards gradually in a spiral stroking motion.

Thighs
Apply pressure with the palms, pushing the skin up as your hands move in circles, working from the knee area to the top of each leg. When using a massager, rotate gradually from the knee area to the top of each leg, covering the whole of each thigh.

Legs
Wrap your hands around one ankle and pull hands gently up to the knee. Repeat several times. Then apply some pressure with four fingers of each hand behind the knee, pulling them up to the top of the leg. Repeat several times and complete by applying finger pressure with four fingers of both hands where the legs join the torso. Apply the same massage technique also to the other leg.

JAPANESE PHILOSOPHY

Taoist Buddhism

The philosophy of Taoism has already been mentioned here, and its teachings have had a profound influence on Oriental and Japanese health and medicine. You don't need to know anything about Taoism to benefit from Japanese health techniques, but it does have much to offer those of us looking for really lasting health and well-being.

The main text on Taoism, the *Tao Te Ching*, was written in the sixth century BC, though even then it was already an old belief. Buddhist monks were largely responsible for the spread of Taoism and T'ai Chi into Japan.

According to Robert Parry, author of *T'ai Chi* (Hodder Headway Lifeguide, 1994), Taoism or the tao is best thought of as the finding of a way. "Way of life", or "way of living" is perhaps the best translation of "tao" for Western readers, but it doesn't fully convey the idea of tao as a path which leads us on a journey towards inner peace of mind and outward sharing of knowledge and wisdom.

Setting out on a personal quest towards tao first begins with learning how to integrate and balance all the opposing and sometimes conflicting elements of your make-up. These opposites are called "Yang" and "Yin", words which are now familiar in the West. The symbol for reconciled and integrated Yang and Yin is actually called the "T'ai Chi" and it is well known in the West. Although the T'ai Chi symbol refers to unities in every sphere, slimmers and the health-conscious can find its imagery very useful. If you think of your body as Yang and your mind as Yin, you can see how the T'ai Chi suggests that both should work together towards the goal of well-being rather than pulling against each other.

Robert Parry concludes: "The central idea of Taoism is that when we as individuals realise our own individual Tao it then becomes indivisible from the greater, universal Tao. Finding one's own way means realising what is essential in one's life."

This emphasis on working together, on discovering positive

qualities in life and in oneself, is very attractive to those brought up in a Northern European background of Protestantism and even Puritanism which stresses one's negative aspects and the need to fight against them. Where Protestant ethics concentrate on mankind's basic state of sin and therefore the need to expiate guilt and atone for wrongdoing, Taoism preaches self-acceptance. It prizes spontaneity and non-violence. Being self-accepting means forgiving yourself for your faults and flaws, but at the same time being humble enough to recognise you have them.

Zen Buddhism

Zen has much in common with Taoism, and indeed it tends to concentrate on just a couple of its ideas, which have been expanded and refined to form a whole philosophy. Zen is another word much used in the West but little understood. Its extreme simplicity and concentration on self-acceptance made it very popular in 1960s California, and to many of us it is inseparable from the hippie movement.

But there is far more to Zen than simply wallowing around in a haze of drug-induced bonhomie. As a branch of Buddhism, Zen originally developed in India in the sixth century AD before moving to China and then Japan. It is said to have been inspired by a teaching of Buddha. At a gathering Buddha simply sat in front of his followers, neither moving nor speaking. Like children in a classroom the followers were at first expectant, then restless, but as the wait grew longer, Buddha eventually had their true full attention. At this point he remained silent, but simply held up a flower to his audience.

The message behind the flower was to encourage his followers to search for abstract truths which are simple to express but complex in significance. Mainstream "flower power" hippie culture of the 1960s was quick to latch onto the simplicity, but by and large failed to probe the complexities.

For true Zen philosophy is rich in complexity and full of interest. It is anti-religious and expresses its teachings in everyday conversation rather than theological language, a technique similar to the Hebrew rabbinical tradition.

It concentrates on essentials and is largely anti-intellectual, resisting attempts to make it logical and rational, or involve its followers in arguments about theoretical concepts. Instead the Zen way of teaching is to demonstrate reality rather than talk about it. A newcomer to Zen has to overcome the tendency to put everything into words.

In her book *Zen: Direct Pointing to Reality* (Thames and Hudson, 1995), Anne Bancroft explains: "Words are essential, but the snag is that when we rely too much on words we begin to substitute a world of indirect knowledge – knowledge about – for the immediate intense impact of what is actually there before thoughts and words arise. By using the right words for each situation, we can live our lives through without ever experiencing anything directly."

The analogy I use for this syndrome is that of 1990s camcorder mania. We have all seen the tourist who never removes his video camcorder from his eye. Presented with the wonders of the Taj Mahal, or when his children see a dolphin for the first time, his reaction is not to see the event personally, but to record it and see it later on his television. A Zen monk would deplore the dependency on cameras and televisions when what we should be using is our eyes and our memories.

So Zen is really about learning to throw away the camcorder and the computer game and instead experience life's adventures directly. Anne Bancroft writes: "Zen aims at helping a pupil see that the conventional ways in which the world is conceptualised are useful for particular purposes but lack substance; when the concept world is broken through, the pupil will come to the experience of the unmediated reality, the discovery of existence itself." One of the most rewarding results of this aspect of Zen is that it helps followers come to terms with reality. It gives them the ability to see life for what it is, and to accept it – and themselves – accordingly. Because of this, Zen followers are noted for their tremendous sense of the absurd, and their humour.

Anne Bancroft writes: "Zen masters when they met each other, would rock with laughter at the idea that they were supposed to be holy and worthy of reverence. They would often caricature each other in portrait form as rotund or absurdly wizened old men, with such titles as a 'bag of rice' or 'snowflake in a hot oven'. They would delightedly set traps, trying to trick each other into conceptual statements about enlightenment or Buddhism or Nirvana, and burst into laughter when the trap was subtly acknowledged or avoided."

Zen really is a most positive life philosophy. For slimming addicts, who are constantly dissatisfied with themselves and their bodies, punishing themselves through unsuccessful dieting, I really do recommend having a little think about Zen. For the rest of us, just trying to feel better physically and mentally, I still think Zen has a lot to offer – and of course, it's always good for a laugh.

13

JAPANESE BEAUTY

Japanese women are renowned not only for their slimness and petiteness but also for their excellent complexions and firm, smooth skin. Few Japanese women ever sigh over a cellulite-dimpled thigh. Some even long for larger bottoms!

But Western women envying them their luck can stop feeling green, because perfect skin and a slender figure don't come naturally to Japanese women — it's the product of their lifestyle; of the diet, health and beauty routines which you are learning about in this book. In Japan many of these routines are shared by men and women alike. The traditional Japanese bath is a unisex activity — rather as saunas are in some parts of Europe — and their relaxing, anti-stress and health promoting qualities are just as helpful to men as to women.

Although racial genetics make Japanese women short and small-boned, it is not just a matter of birth that keeps them slim and youthful looking. You've already discovered how the Japanese stay so slim in the first part of this book. Now it's time to find out how they remain so clear-skinned and youthful looking.

THE JAPANESE BATH

For the Japanese, bath time is about far more than just getting clean. It's a chance for relaxation, rest, sensory pleasure and even socialising with friends in the public bath houses which the Japanese visit as we might go to the local health club and sauna. Equally important, the bath time ritual is the basis of the overall health and beauty routine. Scrubbing, brushing and massaging the skin during washing improves circulation and helps eliminate toxins. It improves the texture and elasticity of the skin, and this firmer skin tone reduces the unsightly surface dimpling caused by cellulite deposits of sub-cutaneous fat (fat beneath the skin). The soaking and aromatherapy techniques used in the bath water also play an important part in relaxing the muscles, warming all parts of the body, increasing suppleness and reducing aches and pains.

Public bathing used to be very much a part of Japanese life. The "sento" or bath house was a centre of Japanese community where people gathered to gossip and relax as well as find a warm refuge from the fiercely cold winters of Northern Japan. Nowadays there are about 12,000 sentos in Japan – but this is far fewer than twenty years ago. It is surprising that the bath house is losing popularity, because its Western equivalent, the sauna and steam room, is getting busier than ever, particularly as part of a health club.

If you have access to a local sauna and steam room, you can have fun using it in the same way the Japanese would use a bath house, substituting the sauna or steam room itself for the hot bath but using all the other beauty routines described in these pages. You may also want to experiment with a cold plunge in between your heat treatments. For those who are strong and fit this is an excellent circulation booster and all-round exhilarator – but don't try it if you have health problems.

The Japanese often use their hot baths as a way of enjoying aromatherapy. They fragrance the water and then allow the aroma-vapour to be absorbed and inhaled while soaking in the bath. On May 5, the day of the Boys' Festival (a children's day of celebration – see page 182), the bath water is filled with iris leaves. At the winter solstice (called "yuzu" – surprisingly close to our word "yule"), the bath is fragrant with orange peel. In the bath routine given here, adding aromatherapy oil at the soaking stage is recommended. Whole books are written on aromatherapy, but here is just a brief guide to help you make up your own aromatherapy oil to add to the bath.

Aromatherapy

You can buy aromatherapy bath oil already made up at most chemists and beauty stores. But personally, I think it is much more fun to make your own. It is very simple. All you need is a small bottle of almond oil; two or three different essential oils; and a small clean empty bottle or jar to mix your oil. Put about a teaspoonful of almond oil into the empty bottle and then add about eight drops of your chosen essential oil or oils. Shake it thoroughly and then add to the bath, making sure you get all the oil out of the bottle (trawl it around in the water). Mix thoroughly, and you have your own personal aromatherapy bath. Here are some of the essential oils you might want to use, together with their properties:

○ Orange/Tangerine – cheering, mood-enhancing, good for fragrance.
○ Lemon Grass – invigorating, toning and cleansing.
○ Geranium – astringent, diuretic, anti-depressant.
○ Tea Tree – antiseptic, germicidal, fungicidal, soothing and healing, skin improver.
○ Sandalwood/Cedarwood – calming, soothing, fragrant.
○ Eucalyptus – de-congestive, strongly vaporous, good for aches and chills.
○ Rosemary – cleansing, stimulating, good for rheumatic pain.
○ Juniper – diuretic, skin toning, sharp.

You can mix two or three oils together in your own recipes. Here are a few combinations that I use:

○ Tangerine and Lemon Grass – very fresh and citrus for energising.
○ Cedarwood and Orange – spicy and warming, perfect for winter time and Christmas.

○ Tea Tree and Geranium – antiseptic, great reviver for blemished winter skins.
○ Rosemary and Juniper – brisk and refreshing for humid summer days.
○ Sandalwood and Tangerine – soothing and sensuous for a luxurious soak.

De-toxifying Skin Cleansers

An important element of the Japanese bathing routine is the exfoliating (removal of dead skin) and de-toxifying process which occurs between washing and the final relaxing soak. This de-toxifying stage is very important if you are using the bath as a health and beauty routine – it is the element that will really improve the tone and texture of your skin.

Originally the Japanese used ground rice grains as their exfoliating, de-toxifying skin cleanser, and several de-toxifying products based on this are available commercially. One of the best ranges, which also has the advantage of being authentic, is made by the Japanese company Kanebo. It includes an exfoliant Body Cleanser, as well as a Japanese-style Wash Mitten (massaging glove). The range also has herbal Bath Salts for your soak and a typically Japanese Whitening Serum for use on skin blemishes after you have bathed. Kanebo products are available from department stores, and good chemists and beauty counters.

There are many other exfoliating skin cleansers and de-toxifying bath salts and soaks on the market. The Body Shop and Boots have good own-brand ranges. Other brands to look for include Princess Marcella Borghese, Thalgo, Montagne Jeunesse and Dior Svelte.

Alternatively you can make your own exfoliating cleanser as follows.

Ingredients:
110g/4oz brown rice; 150g/5oz unroasted peanuts; 1 tsp whole cloves; 50g/2oz coarse grain sea salt; 1 tsp mixed spice.

METHOD:

It is vital that the mixture remains bone dry throughout the process of making it. If moisture gets in, it will lose its keeping quality and its texture. If you don't think you can keep it really dry, make it up in smaller batches and use it all immediately.

In a bone-dry blender whizz the rice, peanuts and cloves until they are reduced to a coarse powder. Pour into a dry mixing bowl and stir in the sea salt and spice, mixing all thoroughly and evenly. Decant the mixture into a clean, dry storage jar – it will make just over 300g/11oz. All the ingredients are organic, so they will deteriorate during storage. To maximise the storage time keep dry, dark and chilled. Once you are confident of the recipe you can make it in smaller, pretty jars to keep in your bathroom.

When you come to using it, scoop a teaspoonful onto your hand, moisten and mix into a paste, then rub onto the skin. Repeat until you have covered all the areas you want.

The Japanese Bath Routine Step by Step

What you will need:

O A deep bath of hot water (the Japanese for bath is "furo" meaning very hot).
O A shower attachment on the bath.
O Aromatherapy bath oil.
O A body brush (a medium-size handled brush with soft bristles, available from chemists and beauty stores).
O A loofah, sisal mitt, or Japanese massage tool (various different types available in Oriental and beauty stores).
O De-toxifying skin cleanser.
O Shampoo.
O Towels.
O Optional – "furoshiki" or Japanese bath towel (see below).
O Optional – "yukata" or Japanese bathrobe (see below).

Japanese bathing happens in two stages. First is the actual washing

215

and cleansing, followed by a therapeutic hot soak. Logically enough, the Japanese prefer not to take their relaxing soak in the same dirty water in which they have just washed. How can you be really clean, they argue, if you have just been lying in water dirty enough to leave a ring round the bath?

It comes as something of a surprise to Westerners that the Japanese solve this problem by not actually washing in the bath itself. They only climb in for a good soak once they are already clean! The actual washing takes place outside the bath on the bathroom floor.

Japanese bathrooms and bath houses are tiled, with drains in the floor, rather like one massive shower room, so washing and rinsing down with plenty of water presents no problem. In the average British bathroom, carpeted and probably full of fluffy bath mats, laundry baskets and so forth, all this water sloshing around simply isn't practical. Nor I think do many of us take kindly to the prospect of standing around naked pouring water over ourselves – the Japanese keep their bathrooms a lot hotter than we do!

So I have adapted the Japanese routine to suit our habits, without losing any of its health and beauty properties.

1. The Big Clean Up

First of all run yourself a hot bath. This will give warmth and steam to the bathroom – important for opening your pores and relaxing your muscles. Don't put anything in the bath at this stage, least of all yourself.

Now it's time to get clean. If you have a separate shower cubicle it is simplest just to take a shower, soaping yourself thoroughly and washing your hair. If you don't, then go back a stage and have a shower standing in the bath before you run the bath.

2. Preparation for De-toxifying

Once you're showered, move to the bath and get in for a quick soak to warm your body so that the next de-toxifying, anti-cellulite stage will be more effective. Those with long hair may want to wrap it in a towel turban for the rest of the bath routine.

3. Skin De-toxifying

Sitting on the edge of the bath, start working the exfoliant, de-toxifying cleanser into your skin. Pay particular attention to problem areas like thighs and bottom, and to areas prone to dryness including chest, shoulders and elbows. Next start brushing your body briskly with the body brush. On the limbs use long, sweeping strokes always working towards the heart. On the torso and bottom use curved strokes ending with a flick up in the direction of the heart. By now your skin should be feeling warm and tingling.

Stand up in the bath and use the shower attachment to rinse down.

4. Massage and Soaking

Next comes the relaxing soak and massage. Add your chosen aromatherapy oil to the bath and stir it well before you sink down into the water. At the beginning of your soak, massage your skin gently using loofah, mitt or Japanese massage tool. Then settle back and relax, breathing deeply to inhale the steamy aromas.

5. Après-bath

When you're quite ready get out and wrap yourself in towels or a Japanese yukata bathrobe. In the Japanese bath house this would be a time for wandering around gossiping and perhaps having a drink of tea or fruit juice – rather as happens in a Western sauna or steam room. If you are at home I suggest you use this period for any personal beauty routines (face masks, etc) or simply for lying down and relaxing. Even if you have to rush off without the customary wind-down period you will still feel warm and revitalised from your bath routine.

The Bathrobe or Yukata

Traditional Japanese used to wear a simple wrap made from hand-dyed indigo cotton when they visited the bath house. These bathrobes gradually became more elaborate, with colourful printed designs of flowers and birds, and many Westerners now wear them as dressing gowns round the house.

Recently though, the original yukata bathrobe has become trendier still, as fashionable young Japanese girls and Western grunge fans have taken to them as summer daywear. Japanese social commentator Elizabeth Kiritani, writes: "Yukati have become the fashionable wear for the young for summer outings, parties and fireworks evenings."

This trend is now taking off in Britain, and you can buy all sorts of yukata at Oriental home stores like Neal Street East and Muji.

The Bath Towel/Bath Sheet – Furoshiki

Ironically, as bathing itself becomes less of a popular public pastime, all things to do with the old bathing traditions are growing more and more fashionable. Along with the yukata bathrobe, the bath spread is now becoming the accessory to have.

Originally the furoshiki bath spread was a large square of cloth which was used to make into a bundle to carry all the bath things to the bath house. On arrival at the bath house it doubled as a mat to stand on when changing and as a spare towel. I suppose the Western equivalent would be rolling a swimming costume up in a towel to go swimming.

Now these squares of fabric have taken on a life as textiles in their own right, with wonderful decorative weaves and prints, and appealing textured fabrics. They come in all sorts of sizes for use as anything from a bedspread to a tablecloth, a throw, a scarf, or even a sarong.

But the truly chic way to use them – or "furo-chic" as fashionable Japanese girls would say – is as wrapping paper. Trendy Japanese stores are beginning to use them for goods instead of carrier bags. No less than 50 million of these furoshiki were sold in 1994.

Elizabeth Kiritani comments: "Young fashionable OLs [office ladies] have been wrapping gifts to one another in fancy furoshiki

– a kind of retro boom considered truly chic. Even Japan's lovely Princess Kiko had her own set of furoshiki order-made."

JAPANESE NATURAL BEAUTY INGREDIENTS

Kanebo is the Tokyo firm which pioneered the use of natural Japanese beauty ingredients in modern cosmetics and skin preparations, and this is why you will see their name mentioned frequently. Originally a textile company back in the 1880s making high-quality silks, Kanebo got into the beauty market when it discovered a protein in silk which proved to be a marvellous skin and hair enhancer.

The substance, silk fibroin, is a water-soluble protein originally developed for use in manufacture of machine-washable silks. Now it is an important active ingredient in Kanebo's wide beauty range, including foundation, dusting powder, skin exfoliants and shampoo. It is partly this success which has encouraged Kanebo to use original Japanese plant extracts throughout its skin care ranges. Kanebo's Chairman Masao Nagata says: "Kanebo is finding new ways to blend modern science with the traditional wisdom of the Orient. Kanebo's herbal medicine, already dominant in pharmacies, is also making a great contribution as medication in hospitals."

Where Japanese companies like Kanebo have led the way, Western beauty houses are following. French companies like Clarins and Thalgo, which already use plant extracts, have been quick to expand their ranges, and many of the Japanese ingredients listed below are found in their formulations. In Britain, Anita Roddick has always believed in borrowing beauty tips from other cultures, and her Body Shop group has sold Japanese Washing Grains for many years.

The newest and most exciting departure though, is the Estée

Lauder Origins range which went on sale in Britain for the first time in 1995. The philosophy behind Origins products of using natural plant-derived therapeutic ingredients is totally in keeping with the Japanese view that good skin, beauty, health and a sense of well-being are inseparable from each other – and that natural, healthy ingredients are what count, whether as part of a skin care routine or of a diet.

GREEN TEA

Western health experts are beginning to get very excited about the healthy nutritional properties of the traditional Japanese green tea drink, but it is also equally effective as a beauty ingredient. Extract of green tea used in Japanese skin products contains vitamin C, amino acids, caffeine and tannin. The caffeine promotes the breakdown of fat and the metabolism of glycogen (a sugar) as well as improving the microcirculation. This helps skin tone and has superficial slimming effects, which are augmented by the firming properties of tannin. This makes skin creams containing green tea extract ideal for use on thighs and bottom and as an all-over skin conditioner. Many Western-produced skin creams and fragrances now contain green tea, but the pioneer in this area is the Japanese company Kanebo, so look out for their Koakuma Cosmetic Body range at department stores, which contains extract of green tea.

GINSENG

Many people discovered ginseng and ginseng tea as a health drink years ago and the original Panax Ginseng was always a highly valued medicine in the East. But it is only fairly recently that it has started to be incorporated as an ingredient in beauty products. The huge explosion in the use of natural vegetable and fruit extracts in skin products was triggered with the discovery of the real improvement in skin brought about by the use of mild acids extracted from fruit and milk. Now even Western cosmetic scientists have realised that ginseng contains active ingredients which work when applied to the skin. Ginseng extract contains amino acids, vitamins and a variety of minerals. It increases circulation in the capillaries, thus improving skin tone and it reduces fatty deposits. Look for it as an ingredient in both facial and body creams. Or make up your own skin rinses using ginseng tea.

SEAWEED EXTRACT
Iodine, potassium, alginic acid and amino acids contribute to the well-known toning, de-toxifying and slimming effects of seaweed-based products. Seaweed extract has an excellent affinity with the skin, which it softens and firms. A great many beauty houses, Western and Japanese, now produce seaweed extract ranges and products – including Thalgo, Biotherm, Clarins, Kanebo, etc. The best way to use seaweed products is during your bathing routine. Use a seaweed-based soak in your bath and choose seaweed extract scrubs and creams to attack cellulite and make your skin smoother and more elastic.

JAPANESE MUGWORT EXTRACT
Mugwort has a long history of medicinal use in the East. It calms itchiness and is seen as an effective choice for treatment of such ailments as generalised skin rashes. It is also an outstanding stimulant to toxin excretion via perspiration, and helps combat fatigue and vulnerability to coldness in the hands and feet. You can find it in Kanebo products, and it is also available in different forms at alternative health centres and health food stores.

POWDERED JAPANESE ANGELICA ROOT
This is a powder made from the dried and pounded roots of the Japanese form of angelica, another plant that has seen long service as an Oriental medicine. It includes such substances as essential oils, vitamin B12, and folic acid. Oriental medicine has used it to great benefit as a sedative and a tonic.

POWDERED UNSHUI PEEL
This was really the first fruit acid, used in Japan to improve the complexion long before the West discovered the powers of vitamin-based acid peels. Unshui is a citrus fruit which contains

essential oils, flavanoid glycoside (an anti-oxidant) and pectin. A powder is made by crushing the peel of the unshui and this is added to skin cream formulations. Like other fruit acids, the unshui peel extract helps rid the skin of old dead cells and gives a fresh, youthful appearance. In Oriental medicine the unshui peel is also used as a digestive aid and a cough treatment.

BENIBANA (SAFFLOWER) EXTRACT

Many people in the West have been recommended by health writers to take safflower capsules as a supplement. It is a rich source of linoleic acid (which combats high cholesterol levels and thrombosis). It is also used therapeutically in the treatment of mild skin complaints like eczema. This benefit to the skin is what the Japanese have latched onto, and they have used safflower as a harmless and beneficial lip colouring for generations. It contains large amounts of flavanoid (anti-oxidant) and effectively promotes the microcirculation.

JAPANESE BURDOCK (GOBO) EXTRACT

Many of us will remember when dandelion and burdock was the parentally approved, "healthy" alternative soft drink to cola, and in fact it is far from a myth that dandelion and burdock both contain active health properties. Dandelion is a well-known diuretic and slimming aid. Burdock is a mild astringent and acts as an excellent skin toner. Extract of Japanese burdock root is an effective moisturiser and is used often as a bath tonic and in other forms of skin treatment in Oriental medicine.

KANZO

Kanzo (botanical name glycyrrhizine) is a rare plant that is particularly treasured in China. It has been used for its medicinal properties for a long time in the East. The glycyrrhizine it contains effectively soothes inflammation arising from ultraviolet ray damage, dryness and other problems associated with skin ageing. Like aloe vera, it is excellent against skin damage, especially due to sunburn. At the moment it is mainly present in Kanebo skin care products, but it will soon be as important in the 1990s as aloe vera was in the 1980s, so look for it soon to be a skin preparation in its own right.

UNPOLISHED RICE

Unpolished brown rice and wheat is a rich source of tocopherol nicotinate. Tocopherol is another name for vitamin E, which we are now discovering to be immensely important in anti-ageing and prevention of disease as part of the A, C and E group of vitamins. It is an anti-oxidant and is one of the few vitamins which has an active impact on the skin when applied directly to its surface rather than being taken nutritionally. It increases cell regeneration which not only promotes healthy, younger-looking skin but also reduces the appearance of burns, stretch marks and scars. Rice in all its forms is fundamental to the Japanese way of life, and rice has been used in cosmetics and beauty routines for centuries. Modern skin preparations which contain rice extract include those by Kanebo.

APRICOT ESSENCE

The kernels of apricots grown in mountainous areas of Central Japan have been prized by herbalists for centuries. Apricot Essence B15 is a rare natural compound extracted from these apricot kernels. Clinical tests have demonstrated the effectiveness of Apricot Essence B15 in promoting cellular regeneration and improving circulation. This ingredient speeds up the skin's turnover cycle and promotes metabolic regeneration, filling out thin tired skin and smoothing out fine wrinkles. Apricot essence is widely used in skin creams, but the pioneer of B15 use is Kanebo.

YOLK LECITHIN

Yolk lecithin is a highly refined and extremely pure biological ingredient that has a remarkable affinity with the skin and remarkable powers of moisture retention. It protects skin from the loss of moisture caused by ageing, and helps keep the skin smooth and firm. If you want to make your own moisturising skin and hair masks, just mix a beaten egg yolk with a little plain cold cream (or even use the egg yolk on its own). Rinse thoroughly afterwards.

ANTI-AGEING TECHNIQUES

After fruit "alpha-hydroxy" acids (AHAs), the next big thing in anti-ageing products is going to be apricot essence. Kanebo was the first company to begin using extracts from apricot kernels in its products and, suspecting that it might work in the same way as AHAs, had the extract clinically tested at Tokushima University. The results were very successful, showing increased cell reproduction, improved circulation in the capillaries on the surface of the skin, and a general enhancement of metabolism in the epidermis. Kanebo now include this ingredient throughout their Sensai Extra Performance Series of anti-ageing products. Other major beauty houses are bound to follow, so when you next visit the beauty counter, keep a look out for anything to do with apricots.

Other natural ingredients which are specifically good for ageing skins include unpolished rice, which stimulates formation of new cells as well as preventing oxidation of oil in pores (the cause of blackheads).

Try switching from a cream to an oil-based cleanser. Oil-based cleansers are equally deep-acting but they are richer for the skin, especially any containing macadamia oil (another traditional Pacific Rim beauty ingredient). Don't be afraid of using an oil-based cleanser if you have oily skin. Oil is actually a very effective solvent of dirt carried within oiliness. Just use the oil first for a really deep cleanse, and then use a very mild soap or cream cleanser to remove any excess oil.

Japanese silk protein has moisture trapping properties which prevent dehydration and keep the skin looking plumper and firmer, and lecithin (in egg yolk) has a similar effect.

Young Skin

It seems you can't win with skin. If your skin isn't looking lined and old due to dehydration and lack of cell renewal, then it's spotty and shiny due to excess oil and rampant cell changes. Many of us feel that we switched straight from greasy young skin to dry old skin with scarcely a day of perfection in between! And, of course, those with combination skins feel as though they are suffering from both kinds of problem skin all their lives.

The secret to preventing this both literally and metaphorically irritating situation is to be aware of exactly what is going on with your skin and be responsive to its needs. It's no good trying to beat oily skin into submission with wince-making astringents and antiseptic washes. Far better to find out about why your skin behaves the way it does (good beauty counters and dieticians will give you plenty of advice), and solve your problems with a recipe of healthy diet and the same natural ingredients applied in your skin care products.

Kanebo has a special Silk Oil Control series of products. Along with silk itself, these contain Chinese peony to control sebum secretion and Japanese comfrey to soothe inflammation and rough skin. And just following the Japanese Diet should have an extremely beneficial effect on your skin.

The Japanese Facial

Have you ever had a professional facial? If so, you'll know that it does far more than just cleanse your face. It leaves you feeling relaxed, rested and rejuvenated. For the Japanese, health and beauty are all part of the same holistic process – eat well, feel well, look well – and the facial is an important element of this. Many beauty counters offer free or discounted facials, so next time you visit a major department store it is worth asking around. Otherwise here is the traditional Japanese routine used by Kanebo (for more details and availability of Kanebo facials, tel: 01635 46362).

Step one: double cleansing
Remove make-up, superficial dirt and secretions with cleansing oil or cleansing lotion. Next exfoliate, either using a mild milk exfoliant or a deeper grainy peeling exfoliant (eg, washing or peeling grains).

Peeling eliminates difficult-to-remove dead skin cells and deposits in the pores, but your skin needs time to regenerate afterwards, so don't use it more than two or three times a week. Don't forget that skin needs looking after below your chin as much as above it, so include neck, throat and upper chest in the whole routine.

Step two: mask
When the skin is very dull and tired it should be treated with a mask, two or three times a week. After deep cleansing, apply the mask thickly onto the skin, and massage for two or three minutes. Allow mask to remain on for up to ten minutes, then rinse off. Some moisturising masks (eg, Clarins) are completely absorbed by the skin and do not need to be rinsed off.

Step three: re-balancing
If you have used a rinse-off mask, pat on a light toning and moisturising lotion or spritz the face with water or an aromatherapy spray. Nelson and Wingate make an excellent aromatherapy spritz (available from larger chemists nationwide).

Step four: treatment
Now is the time to apply your active treatment ingredient. These are usually presented as concentrated essences of which you only need two or three drops. Choose your treatment according to your skin's needs, and follow the instructions. All the major skin care companies carry excellent active treatments, so shop around and please don't be afraid to ask for advice from beauty counter assistants.

Step five: deep moisturising/protection
If you are having your facial before bed, now is the time to apply a really good rich moisturiser, which can work on your skin all night along with the treatment. If you are having your facial during the day, this is the stage where you should apply one of the new wave of protective moisturisers on the market. All the major skin care companies now offer daywear moisturisers which contain UV screens and anti-oxidants to protect your face from

the damaging effects of sunlight and pollution. Look especially for those by Clinique, Kanebo, Clarins and Estée Lauder.

Step six: eye cream

Omit this stage if you are about to put on eye make-up, or if you are under 35. Otherwise pat eye cream gently onto the area above your cheekbones and out to the side. Don't massage or rub eye cream directly onto the upper or lower eyelids – after all, that's not where the wrinkles come, is it? Look out for eye care products by Givenchy, Estée Lauder and Clarins.

Step seven: throat

So many women completely forget to look after their neck and throat until it's too late and they end up with the Joan Collins tortoise look. The skin on your throat, neck and upper chest is if anything even more delicate than on your face, and will show neglect and ageing quicker than anywhere. One rude man once told me that a woman is like a tree – you can tell her age by the number of rings on her neck. So everything you do to your face, extend down over your throat, neck and upper chest – especially cleansing and exfoliating. Finally as you get older, apply the last step of an extra neck firmer and moisturiser. Look out for those by La Prairie, Kanebo, Clarins and Body Shop.

Shiatsu Face Massage

Massage will make your treatment programme even more effective. Using your middle and ring fingers, work your way from the centre of your face, finishing at your temples. With relaxed fingers and moving your arms, massage gently in time with your pulse. Massage two to three times a week after double cleansing. Continue each massage for three minutes.

1. Forehead

Alternate left and right fingers as you gently move from your eyebrows towards your hairline, working diagonally from your left temple to your right temple in twelve steps. Then draw a spiral with your fingertips, moving from the centre of your face toward your temples in six steps finishing with gentle pressure on your temples.

2. Central panel of face
Gently press your upper eyelid, moving toward your temple. On your lower eyelid, press gently toward the outer corner of your eye. Massage your temples in a spiral motion and finish with a downward stroke. Walk your fingers down the sides of your nose, alternating left and right. Massage around the wings of your nose with a kneading motion. Walk your fingers from the centre of your upper lip to the corners of your mouth, then from the centre of your lower lip to the corners of your mouth, alternating left and right.

3. Cheeks
Stroke gently upward toward your temples from your chin, from the corners of your mouth and from the wings of your nose. Draw spirals toward your temples from your chin, from the corners of your mouth, and from the wings of your nose.

4. Neck and chin
Pat gently from your cheeks toward your temples. Press both hands to your face covering the area between chin and temples. Then cover the area between your chin and your earlobes and press gently. Smooth your throat with a downward motion from your chin to your chest.

Acupressure Face and Eye Massage

A traditional Japanese shiatsu massage will increase the effectiveness of products. A massage will loosen muscles, soothe nervous tension and promote the microcirculation at the same time as working together with active ingredients. The thirteen points listed below are for making your skin and face more beautiful. Press each point

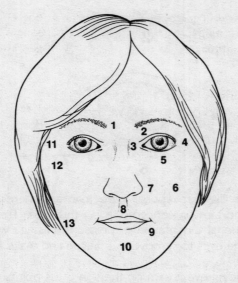

firmly with the middle finger of each hand. This massage can also be performed without cream.

1.   Soothes nerves, promotes restful sleep.
2–6.   Soothes tired eyes, keeps gaze clear and bright. Prevents formation of wrinkles around the eyes.
7.   Stimulates sense of smell.
8–10. Prevents formation of wrinkles round the mouth.
11.   Soothes frayed temper and frazzled nerves.
12.   Relaxes chin and jaw muscles, relieves fatigue.
13.   Stimulates flow of lymph secretions.

Eye Zone

A finger pressure massage increases eye cream effectiveness, as the flow of elastic fibres around the eyes is completely different from that of other parts of the face. As fine wrinkles and sagging

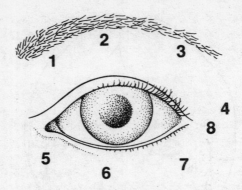

skin are more likely to appear here than anywhere else on the face, it is important to concentrate on this area. Treatment that includes traditional Oriental finger pressure massage works on the skin around the eyes to remove eye fatigue and make fine wrinkles less noticeable.

After spreading eye cream on the skin press points one to eight in that order using the middle finger. The points should be touched lightly at first, then pressed firmly, then the pressure should be gently released.

MAKE-UP TECHNIQUES AND PRODUCTS

Traditional Japanese make-up is of course, far too stylised and formal for us to use in the West, but the techniques are beginning to be increasingly copied by Western professional make-up artists.

In her book *Butterflies of the Night* (Tengu Books, 1992), Lisa Louis describes the process of applying a traditional geisha make-up:

"Making up for the night begins by rubbing on a layer of skin protecting oil from the chest up. Foundation in a shade of bubble-gum pink covers the entire face, but is soon almost completely covered by a brushed-on and then briskly patted layer of stark white. The pink seems to have been unnecessary until one sees that a hazy, rosy glow has skilfully been allowed to emerge in strategic places on the face."

This technique of first correcting the skin to one colour, before applying the desired surface tones, is used by many of today's top catwalk make-up artists. Chanel produces colour-corrective foundations in a glorious range of soft white, pink and glowing yellows. These look far too bright in the bottle to be possible, but when they are correctly applied they conceal lines and shadows, and add any look desired from a golden tan, to English peaches and cream, to ultra-sophisticated. The secret is to copy the geishas and apply one colour on top of another.

Some of the best Japanese make-up products are from Shiseido, the fourth largest cosmetic company in the world. They have recently invented a product which doubles as a moisturiser, foundation and powder (or should that be trebles?) Called Moisture Powder, the product contains spheres which melt on contact with skin and release moisturisers without shine.

Kanebo was the first to introduce the idea of an empty lacquered box which the customer self-fills with magnetic tiles containing blusher, shadow, etc. Very much inspired by the Japanese lacquer box and design traditions, this is now the make-up of choice for the professionals, who delight in having the flexibility to fill a container with exactly what they need.

14

THE DIET FOR LIFE

At the beginning of this book I promised that the Japanese Diet could change your life, and I hope that having read the book and begun to follow the diet you will now agree that this is no empty promise.

The health-giving elements of the Japanese Diet stem both from ingredients and cooking techniques. If your reason for going on the Japanese Diet has been to prevent heart disease or worries about cancer, then you will be particularly keen to make sure you keep eating certain ingredients and using particular cooking methods long after you are no longer following the detailed four weeks of the Japanese Diet.

Look again at the guide to the main ingredients (see page 50) to remind yourself what you need to include in your diet long-term. You will find that substituting rice for other carbohydrates (like potatoes and bread) at some meals is a good idea. Incorporating bean curd and other soya products instead of meat from time to time is also sensible. You'll get the hang of it as you go along. Particularly healthy cooking methods are stir-frying and the sukiyaki method of simmering ingredients in stock – check the cooking methods section again to revise the techniques you'll want to use regularly (see page 73).

For the full health benefits, you really need to make the Japanese Diet a major part of your day-to-day eating in the long term. It is no use expecting to escape heart disease if you are eating a burger and two chocolate bars every day as well as your healthy noodle soup. However, if you can recognise the unhealthy elements of a Western diet – high levels of animal fat; too much sugar; too much junk food; not enough fresh vegetables and fruits – and adapt your Western diet accordingly, you will find that you can fit it in with extra Japanese ingredients very easily.

For slimmers and the health-conscious alike, I think the ideal long-term plan is to reduce the obviously unhealthy Western elements of your diet so that they become occasional celebration and special occasion treats, and on a day-to-day basis bring in the simpler and quicker Japanese recipes to replace some of your Western meals. You may want to continue to use the special Japanese recipes when you have time to shop for them and cook them.

Most people who are interested in Oriental cookery find that it is the cooking methods, the key flavourings and some of the major ingredients that they end up using regularly rather than particular recipes. I now frequently cook meats and stews Oriental-style, and most of my snack meals are based on rice or noodles. You can incorporate Japanese cooking techniques – like stir-frying in small amounts of oil – into your cooking permanently. Certain ingredients like tofu bean curd make a very useful, and cheap, addition to the range of everyday foods we eat, and I hope that some of the recipes, like tempura or sukiyaki, will become special occasion favourites. Japanese-style quick snacks will also be useful as an alternative to equally fast but less nutritious Western junk food.

Now you've discovered how simple and tasty they are, maybe some of the more outlandish things like seaweed and raw fish will get the occasional look-in as well. Even if you are only using it as a bouquet garni to flavour a soup and then removing it before the rest of the family sees the evidence, seaweed can still add its health-giving properties to your diet. And who would have thought when you started that you'd ever give raw fish a try – and like it. Whatever happens, it's my bet that the discoveries you make on your Japanese adventure – both in nutrition and ways of thinking – will become part of your life for ever, just as they did with me.

And as your Japanese cooking takes you on the adventure that is discovering the Japanese way of life and culture, perhaps you'll have time to think more deeply about the aspects of philosophy and traditions I have touched on in this last section of the book.

So much of what I have covered in the Japanese Diet fulfils more than one purpose. A way of eating that keeps you slim also keeps you healthy – but more than that, the thinking behind that cuisine is aimed at promoting your inner health and well-being. Time and again I have discovered that Japanese food ingredients have evolved into beauty products and these in turn serve a purpose in stimulating sensory pleasure.

I hope that your life is enhanced by discovering the holistic benefits of the Japanese Diet, just as mine has been. Among Japanese ladies there used to be a charming custom of passing different fragrances around a gathering, and not smelling, but listening to the aromas. Think about it, and try to hear the wonderful scents that are present in your own life.

BIBLIOGRAPHY OF SOURCES
AND REFERENCES

The author thanks the follow experts for granting interviews:

Dr Tim Key of the Imperial Cancer Research Fund and the EPIC project, Oxford University/Radcliffe Infirmary
Rt Hon Alice Mahon, MP
Professor Richard Peto, Imperial Cancer Research Fund Cancer Studies Unit, Radcliffe Infirmary, Oxford
Professor Karol Sikora, Royal Postgraduate Medical School, Hammersmith Hospital
Dr Chris Williams, Senior Lecturer in Oncology, University of Southampton
Dr Peter Elwood, Medical Research Council, Cardiff University
Allison Coates and Sue Patterson of Bosom Friends
John Brown of the Flora Project, London

Other Sources:

Hugh Faulkner, author of *Against All Odds*, Community Health Foundation, 1992
Simon Brown, Macrobiotic Nutritionist, author of *The Vital Touch*, Community Health Foundation, 1991

Dr Takeshi Hirayoma of the National Cancer Research Institute in Tokyo
European Prospective Investigation into Cancer: Dr Elio Riboli
Professor Michael Oliver of the Royal Brompton National Heart and Lung Institute
British Heart Foundation
Cancer Research Campaign
Health Education Authority
Imperial Cancer Research Fund
Office of Population Censuses and Surveys

Bibliography

R. Peto et al, 'Mortality from smoking in Developed Countries, 1950–2000', World Health Organisation report: *Diet, Nutrition and the Prevention of Chronic Diseases*, Oxford University Press, 1994
C.J.L. Murray and A.D. Lopez, ed., *Global Comparative Assessments in the Health Sector*, World Health Organisation, 1994
G.V. Mann ed., *Coronary Heart Disease: The Dietary Sense and Nonsense*, Janus Publishing, 1993
AG Shaper, *Coronary Heart Disease Risks and Reasons*, Current Medical Literature, 1988
Dr Robert Youngson, *The Antioxidant Health Plan*, Thorsons, 1994
Department of Health, *The Health of the Nation*, HMSO

Journals

Medical Research Council MRC News quarterly
New England Journal of Medicine, USA
The Lancet

USEFUL ADDRESSES

Japan Information and Cultural Centre
Embassy of Japan
101–104 Piccadilly
London W1V 9FN.
Tel: 0171 465 6500

Tesco
Tesco House
Delamare Road
Cheshunt
Waltham Cross
Herts. EN8 9SL
Tel: 01992 632222

Sainsbury
Stamford House
Stamford Street
London SE1 9LL
Tel: 0171 921 6000

Safeway
Aylesford
Nr Maidstone
Kent.
Tel: 01622 712000

Waitrose Ltd
Southern Industrial Area
Bracknell
Berkshire RG12 8YA
Tel: 01344 424680

British T'ai Chi Chuan Association
and London T'ai Chi Academy
Community Health Foundation
7 Upper Wimpole Street
London W1M 7TD
Tel: 0171 251 4076

The Shiatsu Society
Answering service
Tel: 01483 860771

London College of Shiatsu
1 Central Park Lodge
54–58 Bolsover Street
London W1P 7HL
Tel: 0171 383 2619

The British School of Shiatsu-Do
6 Erskine Road
London NW3 3AJ
Tel: 0171 483 3776

Kanebo
5 Bone Lane
Newbury
Berkshire
Tel: 01635 46362

Shiseido
Ivory Place
Treadgold Street
London W11 4BP
Tel: 0171 792 4575

Japanese Canadian Cultural Centre
123 Wynford Drive
Don Mills
ON M3C 2S2
Canada
Tel: (416) 441 2345

Japanese Food Ozawa
135 East Beaver Creek Road
Thornhill
ON L4B 1E2
Canada
Tel: (416) 229 6343

Shiatsu School of Canada Kaz Kamiya
547 College Street
Toronto
ON M6G 4A2
Canada
Tel: (416) 323 3700

INDEX

General index.
For recipes see the separate index of recipes.

239

Index of recipes.